HOUGHTON MIFFLIN HARCOURT

Response to Intervention

FOR THE COMMON CORE STATE STANDARDS FOR MATHEMATICS

GRADE 2

**PROVIDES Tier 1 Intervention for
Every Common Core Standard**

HOUGHTON MIFFLIN HARCOURT

Printed in the U.S.A.

ISBN 978-0-547-83620-1

5 6 7 8 9 10   0982   21 20 19 18 17 16 15 14 13

4500404099   B C D E F G

Table of Contents

Operations and Algebraic Thinking

Number and Operations in Base Ten

▶ **Understand place value.**

▶ **Use place value understanding and properties of operations to add and subtract.**

Measurement and Data

► **Represent and interpret data.**

Geometry

► **Reason with shapes and their attributes.**

LESSON 1

Algebra • Use Drawings to Represent Problems

OBJECTIVE Use bar models to represent a variety of addition and subtraction situations.

CC.2.OA.1

You can use bar models to show problems.

There are 5 girls and 11 boys at the park.
How many more boys than girls are at the park?

How many boys?

11

How many girls?

5	

_6_

Write a number sentence. $11 - 5 = 6$

There are _6_ more boys than girls.

Complete the bar model. Then write a number sentence to solve.

1. Nathan had 7 stamps. Then he got 9 more stamps.
   How many stamps does Nathan have now?

7	9

____

____ + ____ = ____   ____ stamps

CC.2.OA.1

Algebra • Use Drawings to Represent Problems

Complete the bar model. Then write a number sentence to solve.

1. Sara has 4 yellow beads
and 3 green beads.
How many beads does
Sara have?

4	3

_____

_____

_____ beads

---

2. Adam had 12 trucks.
He gave 4 trucks to Ed.
How many trucks does
Adam have now?

____	4

12

_____

_____ trucks

---

3. Grandma has 14 red
roses and 7 pink roses.
How many more red
roses than pink roses
does she have?

14

7	

_____

_____

_____ more red roses

LESSON 2 **Algebra • Use Equations to Represent Problems**

CC.2.OA.1

OBJECTIVE Write equations to represent and solve a variety of addition and subtraction situations.

Some red fish and 9 green fish are in a tank.
The tank has 14 fish. How many red fish are there?

9	?

_14_

Write a number sentence.

Use a for the missing number.

$$14 - 9 = \blacksquare$$

_5_ red fish in the tank.

Write a number sentence for the problem.
Use a ▮ for the missing number. Then solve.

1. There are 13 trees in a park.
   8 are pine trees. The rest are
   oak trees. How many oak trees
   are there?

   So there are _____

   _____ oak trees.

8	?

_13_

Algebra • Use Equations to Represent Problems

Write a number sentence for the problem.
Use a ▮ **for the missing number. Then solve.**

1. There were 15 apples in a bowl. Dan used some apples to make a pie. Now there are 7 apples in the bowl. How many apples did Dan use?

_____

_____ apples

2. Amy has 16 gift bags. She fills 8 gift bags with whistles. How many gift bags are not filled with whistles?

_____

_____ gift bags

3. There were 5 dogs at the park. Then 9 more dogs joined them. How many dogs are at the park now?

_____

_____ dogs

Problem Solving

Write or draw to show how you solved the problem.

4. Tony has 7 blue cubes and 6 red cubes. How many cubes does he have in all?

_____ cubes

LESSON 3 **Problem Solving · Addition**

OBJECTIVE Solve problems involving 2-digit addition by using the strategy *draw a diagram.*

CC.2.OA.1

Hannah has 14 pencils. Juan has 13 pencils.
How many pencils do they have in all?

Unlock the Problem

What do I need to find?	**What information do I need to use?**
how many pencils	Hannah has __14__ pencils.
they have in all	Juan has __13__ pencils.

Show how to solve the problem.

Hannah's 14 pencils	Juan's 13 pencils

_____ ? pencils in all

14 + 13 = ■   __27__ pencils

Solve.

1. There are 21 peanuts in a bag. 16 more
   peanuts are put into the bag. How many
   peanuts are in the bag in all?

21 peanuts	16 peanuts

_____ peanuts in all   _____ peanuts

Problem Solving · Addition

Label the bar model. Write a number sentence with a ▪ for the missing number. Solve.

1. Jacob counts 37 ants on the sidewalk and 11 ants on the grass. How many ants does Jacob count?

_____

_____ ants

2. There are 14 bees in the hive and 17 bees in the garden. How many bees are there in all?

_____

_____ bees

3. There are 28 flowers in Sasha's garden. 16 flowers are yellow and the rest are white. How many white flowers are in Sasha's garden?

_____

_____ white flowers

LESSON 4

Algebra • Write Equations to Represent Addition

OBJECTIVE Represent addition situations with number sentences using a symbol for the unknown number.

CC.2.OA.1

Sara took 16 pictures.

Then she took 17 more pictures.

How many pictures did Sara take in all?

Use a bar model to show the problem.

16 pictures	17 pictures

___?__ pictures in all

Write a number sentence. Solve.

$$16 + 17 = \blacksquare \qquad \underline{33} \text{ pictures}$$

Use a bar model to show the problem. Write a number sentence. Use a ■ **for the missing number. Then solve.**

1. Josh has 18 basketball cards and 14 baseball cards. How many cards does he have altogether?

_____ basketball cards	_____ baseball cards

_____ cards altogether

_____   ____ cards

Algebra • Write Equations to Represent Addition

Write a number sentence for the problem.
Use a ▨ for the missing number. Then solve.

1. Emily and her friends went to the park. They saw 15 robins and 9 blue jays. How many birds did they see?

_____

_____ birds

2. Joe has 13 fish in one tank. He has 8 fish in another tank. How many fish does Joe have?

_____

_____ fish

Problem Solving

Solve.

3. There are 21 children in Kathleen's class. 12 of the children are girls. How many children in her class are boys?

_____ boys

© Houghton Mifflin Harcourt Publishing Company

LESSON 5 **Problem Solving • Subtraction**
OBJECTIVE Solve problems involving 2-digit subtraction by using the strategy *draw a diagram*.

 CC.2.OA.1

Katie had a box of 42 craft sticks. She used 26 craft sticks to make a sailboat. How many craft sticks were not used?

Unlock the Problem

What do I need to find?

how many craft sticks
_____
were not used

What information do I need to use?

Katie had 42 craft sticks .

She used 26 craft sticks .

Show how to solve the problem.

42 -- 26 == ■
_____

16 craft sticks

Write a number sentence with a ■ for the missing number. Solve.

1. Ms. Lee took 35 purses to the fair. She sold 14 purses. How many purses does she have left?

_____   _____ purses

CC.2.OA.1

Problem Solving · Subtraction

**Label the bar model. Write a
number sentence with a ▇ for
the missing number. Solve.**

1. Megan picked 34 flowers. Some
of the flowers are yellow and
18 flowers are pink. How many
of the flowers are yellow?

_____ yellow flowers

_____

2. Alex had 45 toy cars. He put
26 toy cars in a box. How many
toy cars are not in the box?

_____ toy cars

_____

3. Mr. Kane makes 43 pizzas. 28 of
the pizzas are small. The rest are
large. How many pizzas are large?

_____ large pizzas

_____

LESSON 6

Algebra • Write Equations to Represent Subtraction

CC.2.OA.1

OBJECTIVE Represent subtraction situations with number sentences using a symbol for the unknown number.

---

37 birds were in the trees.

13 birds flew away.

How many birds are in the trees now?

The bar model shows the problem.

13	?

37

Use the bar model to write a number sentence.

$37 - 13 = $ ■

Subtract to find the missing part.

So, the answer is __24__ birds.

$$\begin{array}{r} 37 \\ -13 \\ \hline 24 \end{array}$$

Write a number sentence for the problem.

Use a ■ **for the missing number. Then solve.**

I. Gina has 23 pens. 15 pens are blue and the rest are red. How many pens are red?

15	?

23

_____

_____ red pens

Algebra • Write Equations to Represent Subtraction

Write a number sentence for the problem.
Use a ▦ for the missing number. Then solve.

I. 29 children rode their bikes
to school. After some of the
children rode home, there were
8 children with bikes still at school.
How many children rode their
bikes home?

_____   _____ children

2. 32 children were on the school
bus. Then 24 children got off
the bus. How many children were
still on the bus?

_____   _____ children

Problem Solving

Solve. Write or draw to explain.

3. There were 21 children in the library.
After 7 children left the library, how many
children were still in the library?

_____ children

© Houghton Mifflin Harcourt Publishing Company

LESSON 7

Solve Multistep Problems

OBJECTIVE Analyze word problems to determine what operations to use to solve multistep problems.

Mr. Wright had 34 blue pencils and 25 red pencils. He gave 42 pencils to students. How many pencils does he have now?

The first sentence tells you what Mr. Wright had.

and

$$\begin{array}{r} 34 \\ +25 \\ \hline 59 \end{array}$$

blue pencils   red pencils

The second sentence tells you that he gave 42 of the pencils to students.

pencils

$$\begin{array}{r} 59 \\ -42 \\ \hline 17 \end{array}$$

Mr. Wright has __17__ pencils now.

Solve the problem in steps. Show what you did.

1. Kara had 37 stickers. She gave 11 stickers to Sam and 5 stickers to Jane. How many stickers does Kara have now?

_____ stickers

Solve Multistep Problems

Complete the bar models for the steps you do to solve the problem.

1. Greg has 60 building blocks. His sister gives him 17 more blocks. He uses 38 blocks to make a tower. How many blocks are not used in the tower?

_____ blocks

2. Jenna has a train of 26 connecting cubes and a train of 37 connecting cubes. She gives 15 cubes to a friend. How many cubes does Jenna have now?

_____ cubes

Problem Solving

Solve. Write or draw to explain.

3. Ava has 25 books. She gives away 7 books. Then Tom gives her 12 books. How many books does Ava have now?

_____ books

LESSON 8 — Use Doubles Facts

OBJECTIVE Use doubles facts as a strategy for finding sums for near doubles facts.

CC.2.OA.2

Use doubles facts to help you find sums.

If you know 6 + 6,
you can find 6 + 7.

$$\underline{6} + \underline{6} = \underline{12}$$

7 is 1 more than 6.
So, 6 + 7 is 1 more than 6 + 6.

$$\underline{6} + \underline{7} = \underline{13}$$

**Write a doubles fact you can use
to find the sum. Write the sum.**

1. 4 + 5 = _____   _____ + _____ = _____

2. 5 + 6 = _____   _____ + _____ = _____

3. 7 + 8 = _____   _____ + _____ = _____

4. 8 + 9 = _____   _____ + _____ = _____

Operations and Algebraic Thinking

CC.2.OA.2

Use Doubles Facts

**Write a doubles fact you can use
to find the sum. Write the sum.**

1. 2 + 3 = _____

_____ + _____ = _____

2. 7 + 6 = _____

_____ + _____ = _____

3. 3 + 4 = _____

_____ + _____ = _____

4. 8 + 9 = _____

_____ + _____ = _____

5. 6 + 5 = _____

_____ + _____ = _____

6. 4 + 5 = _____

_____ + _____ = _____

Problem Solving

Solve. Write or draw to explain.

7. There are 6 ants on a log. Then 7 ants
crawl onto the log. How many ants
are on the log now?

_____ ants

© Houghton Mifflin Harcourt Publishing Company

Practice Addition Facts

LESSON 9

OBJECTIVE Recall sums for basic facts using properties and strategies.

CC.2.OA.2

Use what you know to find sums.

☆☆☆ ★★★★★

Add in any order.

$3 + 5 = \underline{8}$

★★★★★ ☆☆☆

If you know $3 + 5$,
then you know $5 + 3$.

$5 + 3 = \underline{8}$

Count on to add. To add 1, 2, or 3 to any ☆☆☆☆☆ ★
number, count on from that number.

$5 + 1 = \underline{6}$

Write the sums.

1. $5 + 7 = \underline{\hspace{1cm}}$

$7 + 5 = \underline{\hspace{1cm}}$

2. $\underline{\hspace{1cm}} = 5 + 1$

$\underline{\hspace{1cm}} = 5 + 2$

3. $6 + 2 = \underline{\hspace{1cm}}$

$6 + 3 = \underline{\hspace{1cm}}$

4. $\underline{\hspace{1cm}} = 9 + 5$

$\underline{\hspace{1cm}} = 5 + 9$

5. $7 + 3 = \underline{\hspace{1cm}}$

$3 + 7 = \underline{\hspace{1cm}}$

6. $5 + 2 = \underline{\hspace{1cm}}$

$5 + 3 = \underline{\hspace{1cm}}$

7. $\underline{\hspace{1cm}} = 3 + 6$

$\underline{\hspace{1cm}} = 6 + 3$

8. $4 + 1 = \underline{\hspace{1cm}}$

$1 + 4 = \underline{\hspace{1cm}}$

9. $8 + 2 = \underline{\hspace{1cm}}$

$8 + 3 = \underline{\hspace{1cm}}$

Practice Addition Facts

Write the sums.

1. $9 + 1 = $ _____

$1 + 9 = $ _____

2. $7 + 6 = $ _____

$6 + 7 = $ _____

3. $8 + 0 = $ _____

$5 + 0 = $ _____

4. _____ $= 7 + 9$

_____ $= 9 + 7$

5. $4 + 4 = $ _____

$4 + 5 = $ _____

6. $9 + 9 = $ _____

$9 + 8 = $ _____

7. $8 + 8 = $ _____

$8 + 7 = $ _____

8. $2 + 2 = $ _____

$2 + 3 = $ _____

9. _____ $= 6 + 3$

_____ $= 3 + 6$

10. $6 + 6 = $ _____

$6 + 7 = $ _____

11. _____ $= 0 + 7$

_____ $= 0 + 9$

12. $5 + 5 = $ _____

$5 + 6 = $ _____

13. $8 + 5 = $ _____

$5 + 8 = $ _____

14. $8 + 2 = $ _____

$2 + 8 = $ _____

15. $7 + 4 = $ _____

$4 + 7 = $ _____

Problem Solving

Solve. Write or draw to explain.

16. Jason has 7 puzzles. Quincy has the same number of puzzles as Jason. How many puzzles do they have altogether?

_____ puzzles

LESSON 10

Algebra • Make a Ten to Add

OBJECTIVE Recall sums for addition facts using the make a ten strategy.

 CC.2.OA.2

$8 + 5 =$ ___?___

Step 1 Start with the greater addend.
Break apart the other addend to make a ten.

8 $+$ 5

Step 2 You need to add **2** to 8 to make a ten. So, break apart 5 as **2** and 3.

$8 + 2 = 10$ 3

Step 3 Add on the rest to the 10. $10 +$ __3__ $=$ __13__

Step 4 Write the sum. $8 + 5 =$ __13__

Show how you can make a ten to find the sum. Write the sum.

1. $7 + 6 =$ ___

3 3

$10 +$ ___ $=$ ___

2. $9 + 2 =$ ___

1 1

$10 +$ ___ $=$ ___

3. $4 + 8 =$ ___

2 2

$10 +$ ___ $=$ ___

4. $5 + 9 =$ ___

$10 +$ ___ $=$ ___

5. $8 + 6 =$ ___

$10 +$ ___ $=$ ___

6. $4 + 9 =$ ___

$10 +$ ___ $=$ ___

Algebra • Make a Ten to Add

Show how you can make a ten to find the sum.
Write the sum.

1. $9 + 7 =$ _____

$10 +$ _____ $=$ _____

2. $8 + 5 =$ _____

$10 +$ _____ $=$ _____

3. $8 + 6 =$ _____

$10 +$ _____ $=$ _____

4. $3 + 9 =$ _____

$10 +$ _____ $=$ _____

5. $8 + 7 =$ _____

$10 +$ _____ $=$ _____

6. $6 + 5 =$ _____

$10 +$ _____ $=$ _____

7. $7 + 6 =$ _____

$10 +$ _____ $=$ _____

8. $5 + 9 =$ _____

$10 +$ _____ $=$ _____

Problem Solving

Solve. Write or draw to explain.

9. There are 9 children on the bus. Then 8 more children get on the bus. How many children are on the bus now?

_____ children

LESSON 11

Algebra • Add 3 Addends

OBJECTIVE Find sums of three addends by applying the Commutative and Associative Properties of Addition.

CC.2.OA.2

Add numbers in any order.
The sum stays the same.

$1 + 4 + 6 = $ | |

$5 + 6 = $ | |

$1 + 4 + 6 = $ | |

$1 + 10 = $ | |

$1 + 4 + 6 = $ | |

$7 + 4 = $ | |

Solve two ways. Circle the two addends you add first.

1. $2 + 3 + 2 = $ _____ $2 + 3 + 2 = $ _____

2. $7 + 2 + 3 = $ _____ $7 + 2 + 3 = $ _____

3. $1 + 1 + 9 = $ _____ $1 + 1 + 9 = $ _____

4. $6 + 4 + 4 = $ _____ $6 + 4 + 4 = $ _____

Algebra · Add 3 Addends

Solve two ways. Circle the two addends you add first.

1. $2 + 3 + 7 =$ _____ $2 + 3 + 7 =$ _____

2. $5 + 3 + 3 =$ _____ $5 + 3 + 3 =$ _____

3. $4 + 5 + 4 =$ _____ $4 + 5 + 4 =$ _____

4. $4 + 4 + 4 =$ _____ $4 + 4 + 4 =$ _____

5.

$$\begin{array}{r} 5 \\ 4 \\ +5 \\ \hline \end{array} \qquad \begin{array}{r} 5 \\ 4 \\ +5 \\ \hline \end{array}$$

6.

$$\begin{array}{r} 6 \\ 3 \\ +4 \\ \hline \end{array} \qquad \begin{array}{r} 6 \\ 3 \\ +4 \\ \hline \end{array}$$

Problem Solving

Choose a way to solve. Write or draw to explain.

7. Amber has 2 red crayons, 5 blue crayons, and 4 yellow crayons. How many crayons does she have in all?

_____ crayons

LESSON 12

Algebra · Relate Addition and Subtraction

OBJECTIVE Use the inverse relationship of addition and subtraction to recall basic facts.

CC.2.OA.2

Use addition facts to help you subtract.

$8 + 7 = 15$

Think of $8 + 7 = 15$ to find the difference for a related fact:

$15 - 7 =$ _____.

$15 - 7 = \underline{8}$

Write the sum and the difference for the related facts.

1. $6 + 3 =$ _____

$9 - 6 =$ _____

2. $7 + 6 =$ _____

$13 - 7 =$ _____

3. $6 + 8 =$ _____

$14 - 8 =$ _____

4. $7 + 4 =$ _____

$11 - 7 =$ _____

5. $8 + 4 =$ _____

$12 - 4 =$ _____

6. $8 + 8 =$ _____

$16 - 8 =$ _____

7. $9 + 7 =$ _____

$16 - 7 =$ _____

8. $7 + 5 =$ _____

$12 - 7 =$ _____

CC.2.OA.2

Algebra · Relate Addition and Subtraction

Write the sum and the difference for the related facts.

1. $9 + 6 =$ _____

$15 - 6 =$ _____

2. $8 + 5 =$ _____

$13 - 5 =$ _____

3. $9 + 9 =$ _____

$18 - 9 =$ _____

4. $7 + 3 =$ _____

$10 - 3 =$ _____

5. $7 + 5 =$ _____

$12 - 5 =$ _____

6. $6 + 8 =$ _____

$14 - 6 =$ _____

7. $6 + 7 =$ _____

$13 - 6 =$ _____

8. $8 + 8 =$ _____

$16 - 8 =$ _____

9. $6 + 4 =$ _____

$10 - 4 =$ _____

10. $7 + 9 =$ _____

$16 - 9 =$ _____

11. $9 + 4 =$ _____

$13 - 9 =$ _____

12. $8 + 7 =$ _____

$15 - 7 =$ _____

Problem Solving

Solve. Write or draw to explain.

13. There are 13 children on the bus. Then 5 children get off the bus. How many children are on the bus now?

_____ children

Name _____

LESSON 13 **Practice Subtraction Facts**

OBJECTIVE Recall differences for basic facts using mental strategies.

CC.2.OA.2

Here are two ways to find differences.

$$10 - 3 = \underline{\quad ? \quad}$$

Count back 1, 2, or 3.

5   6   7   8   9   10   11

$10 - 1 = \underline{\quad 9 \quad}$

$10 - 2 = \underline{\quad 8 \quad}$

$10 - 3 = \underline{\quad 7 \quad}$

Think of a related addition fact.

$3 + 7 = \underline{\quad 10 \quad}$

so, $10 - 3 = \underline{\quad 7 \quad}$

Write the difference.

1. $13 - 5 = \underline{\qquad}$

2. $10 - 4 = \underline{\qquad}$

3. $12 - 3 = \underline{\qquad}$

4. $11 - 2 = \underline{\qquad}$

5. $9 - 3 = \underline{\qquad}$

6. $12 - 5 = \underline{\qquad}$

7. $16 - 8 = \underline{\qquad}$

8. $13 - 7 = \underline{\qquad}$

CC.2.OA.2

Practice Subtraction Facts

Write the difference.

1. $15 - 9 =$ _____   **2.** $10 - 2 =$ _____   **3.** _____ $= 13 - 5$

4. $14 - 7 =$ _____   **5.** $10 - 8 =$ _____   **6.** $12 - 7 =$ _____

7. _____ $= 10 - 3$ **8.** $16 - 7 =$ _____   **9.** $8 - 4 =$ _____

10. $11 - 5 =$ _____   **11.** $13 - 6 =$ _____   **12.** _____ $= 12 - 9$

13. $16 - 9 =$ _____   **14.** _____ $= 11 - 9$ **15.** $12 - 8 =$ _____

16. $14 - 8 =$ _____   **17.** $10 - 5 =$ _____   **18.** $12 - 5 =$ _____

19. $15 - 7 =$ _____   **20.** $14 - 9 =$ _____   **21.** $17 - 9 =$ _____

Problem Solving

Solve. Write or draw to explain.

22. Mr. Li has 16 pencils. He gives 9 pencils to some students. How many pencils does Mr. Li have now?

_____ pencils

Name _____

LESSON 14 **Use Ten to Subtract**

OBJECTIVE Find differences using models to develop the mental strategy of decomposing to simplify facts.

CC.2.OA.2

You can get to ten to help find differences.

$$13 - 7 = \underline{\ ?\ }$$

Step ① Start with the first number.

Step ② Subtract ones to get to 10.

$$13 - 3 = 10$$

Step ③ Subtract the rest from the 10.

Think: I had 13. I subtracted 3 to get to 10. Now I subtract the 4 I have left.

$$10 - \underline{4} = \underline{6}$$

Step ④ Write the difference.

$$13 - 7 = \underline{6}$$

Show the tens fact you used. Write the difference.

1. $15 - 8 =$ _____

5   3

$10 - \underline{3} =$ _____

2. $12 - 4 =$ _____

2   2

$10 - \underline{\ \ } =$ _____

3. $11 - 7 =$ _____

6   1

$10 - \underline{\ \ } =$ _____

4. $13 - 5 =$ _____

3   2

$10 - \underline{\ \ } =$ _____

© Houghton Mifflin Harcourt Publishing Company

Operations and Algebraic Thinking

27

CC.2.OA.2

Use Ten to Subtract

Show the tens fact you used. Write the difference.

1. $14 - 6 =$ _____

$10 -$ _____ $=$ _____

2. $12 - 7 =$ _____

$10 -$ _____ $=$ _____

3. $13 - 7 =$ _____

$10 -$ _____ $=$ _____

4. $15 - 8 =$ _____

$10 -$ _____ $=$ _____

5. $11 - 7 =$ _____

$10 -$ _____ $=$ _____

6. $14 - 5 =$ _____

$10 -$ _____ $=$ _____

Problem Solving

Solve. Write or draw to explain.

7. Carl read 15 pages on Monday night and 9 pages on Tuesday night. How many more pages did he read on Monday night than on Tuesday night?

_____ more pages

LESSON 15

Algebra • Even and Odd Numbers

OBJECTIVE Classify numbers up to 20 as even or odd.

 CC.2.OA.3

These are even numbers.
They show pairs with no cubes left over.

4 is even.   6 is even.   8 is even.   10 is even.

These are odd numbers.
They show pairs with 1 cube left over.

3 is odd.   5 is odd.   7 is odd.   9 is odd.

Count out the number of cubes.
Make pairs. Then write even or odd.

1. 15 _____	**2.** 11 _____
3. 12 _____	**4.** 13 _____
5. 16 _____	**6.** 14 _____

CC.2.OA.3

Algebra • Even and Odd Numbers

Shade in the ten frames to show the number.
Circle even or odd.

1.   15

even   odd

2.   18

even   odd

3.   11

even   odd

4.   17

even   odd

5.   13

even   odd

6.   20

even   odd

Problem Solving

7. Mr. Dell has an odd number of sheep and an even number of cows on his farm. Circle the choice that could tell about his farm.

9 sheep and 10 cows

10 sheep and 11 cows

8 sheep and 12 cows

© Houghton Mifflin Harcourt Publishing Company

LESSON 16

Algebra • Represent Even Numbers

OBJECTIVE Write equations with equal addends to represent even numbers.

 CC.2.OA.3

An even number of cubes will make two equal groups.

Count 8 cubes. Put the cubes into two equal groups. Do the two groups have equal numbers of cubes? To check, match one to one.

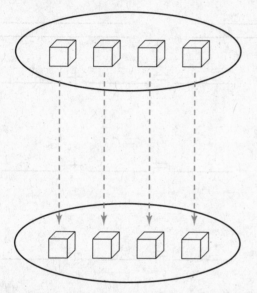

$8 = \underline{} + \underline{}$

How many cubes are there in all? Complete the addition sentence to show the equal groups.

1. $\underline{} = \underline{} + \underline{}$

2. $\underline{} = \underline{} + \underline{}$

3. $\underline{} = \underline{} + \underline{}$

4. $\underline{} = \underline{} + \underline{}$

CC.2.OA.3

Algebra • Represent Even Numbers

Shade in the frames to show two equal groups for each
number. Complete the addition sentence to show the groups.

1. 8

_____ = _____ + _____

2. 18

_____ = _____ + _____

3. 10

_____ = _____ + _____

4. 14

_____ = _____ + _____

5. 20

_____ = _____ + _____

6. 12

_____ = _____ + _____

Problem Solving

Solve. Write or draw to explain.

7. The seats in a van are in pairs. There
    are 16 seats. How many pairs of seats
    are there?

_____ pairs of seats

LESSON 17

Problem Solving · Equal Groups

OBJECTIVE Solve problems involving equal groups by using the strategy *act it out.*

CC.2.OA.4

Clarence puts grapes in 4 rows. He puts 5 grapes in each row.
How many grapes does Clarence have?

Unlock the Problem

What do I need to find?	**What information do I need to use?**
## how many grapes Clarence has	Clarence has __4__ rows of grapes. He puts __5__ grapes in each row.

Show how to solve the problem.

○○○○○
○○○○○
○○○○○
○○○○○

Clarence has __20__ grapes.

Draw to show what you did.

1. Rachel puts her markers in 3 rows.
   Each row has 3 markers.
   How many markers does Rachel have?

Rachel has _____ markers.

CC.2.OA.4

Problem Solving • Equal Groups

Act out the problem.
Draw to show what you did.

1. Mr. Anderson has 4 plates of cookies. There are 5 cookies on each plate. How many cookies are there in all?

    _____ cookies

2. Ms. Trane puts some stickers in 3 rows. There are 2 stickers in each row. How many stickers does Ms. Trane have?

    _____ stickers

3. There are 5 books in each box. How many books are in 5 boxes?

    _____ books

LESSON 18

Algebra • Repeated Addition

OBJECTIVE Write equations using repeated addition to find the total number of objects in arrays.

Find the total number of cats.

- Circle each row.
- Count how many rows.

  _3_ equal rows

- Count how many in one row.

  _4_ cats in one row

- Write an addition sentence. Add the number of cats in each row.

_4_ + _4_ + _4_ = _12_

Find the number of shapes in each row.
Complete the addition sentence to find the total.

1. ●●●●●   3 rows of _____
   ●●●●●
   ●●●●●

   ____ + ____ + ____ = ____

2. ✕ ✕ ✕ ✕   4 rows of _____
   ✕ ✕ ✕ ✕
   ✕ ✕ ✕ ✕
   ✕ ✕ ✕ ✕

   ____ + ____ + ____ + ____ = ____

Algebra · Repeated Addition

Find the number of shapes in each row.
Complete the addition sentence to find the total.

1.

3 rows of ____

____ + ____ + ____ = ____

2.

2 rows of ____

____ + ____ = ____

3.

4 rows of ____

____ + ____ + ____ + ____ = ____

4.

4 rows of ____

____ + ____ + ____ + ____ = ____

Problem Solving

Solve. Write or draw to explain.

5. A classroom has 3 rows of desks.
There are 5 desks in each row. How
many desks are there altogether?

____ desks

LESSON 19

Explore 3-Digit Numbers

OBJECTIVE Write 3-digit numbers that are represented by groups of tens.

 CC.2.NBT.1

---

10 tens

_1_ _1_ tens

_1_ hundred _1_ ten

_110_

---

10 tens

_1_ _2_ tens

_1_ hundred _2_ tens

_120_

---

10 tens

_1_ _3_ tens

_1_ hundred _3_ tens

_130_

Circle tens to make 1 hundred. Write the number in different ways.

1.

_____ tens

_____ hundred _____ tens

2.

_____ tens

_____ hundred _____ tens

_____

Name _____

CC.2.NBT.1

Explore 3-Digit Numbers

Circle tens to make 1 hundred. Write the
number in different ways.

1.

_____ tens

_____ hundred _____ tens

_____

2.

_____ tens

_____ hundred _____ tens

_____

3.

_____ tens

_____ hundred _____ tens

_____

Problem Solving

Solve. Write or draw to explain.

4. Millie has a box of 1 hundred cubes.
She also has a bag of 70 cubes.
How many trains of 10 cubes
can she make?

_____ trains of 10 cubes

Lesson 19

LESSON 20

Model 3-Digit Numbers

OBJECTIVE Use concrete and pictorial models to represent 3-digit numbers.

CC.2.NBT.1

Show 243.

Hundreds	Tens	Ones

With blocks:

In a chart:

Hundreds	Tens	Ones
2	4	3

With a quick picture:

Write how many hundreds, tens, and ones.
Show with ▦▮▫. Then draw a quick picture.

1. 138

Hundreds	Tens	Ones

2. 217

Hundreds	Tens	Ones

3. 352

Hundreds	Tens	Ones

4. 174

Hundreds	Tens	Ones

Model 3-Digit Numbers

Write how many hundreds, tens, and ones.
Show with ▦ ▌ **..** **Then draw a quick picture.**

1. 118

Hundreds	Tens	Ones

2. 246

Hundreds	Tens	Ones

3. 143

Hundreds	Tens	Ones

4. 237

Hundreds	Tens	Ones

Problem Solving

5. Write the number that matches the clues.

- My number has 2 hundreds.

- The tens digit is 9 more than the ones digit.

Hundreds	Tens	Ones

My number is _____.

LESSON 21

Hundreds, Tens, and Ones

OBJECTIVE Apply place value concepts to write 3-digit numbers that are represented by pictorial models.

How many are there in all?

Hundreds	Tens	Ones

___3___ hundreds ___2___ tens ___5___ ones

Write how many in the chart.

Hundreds	Tens	Ones
3	2	5

Write the number as hundreds plus tens plus ones.

___300___ + ___20___ + ___5___

3 hundreds 2 tens 5 ones is the same as ___325___.

Write how many hundreds, tens, and ones are in the model. Write the number in two ways.

1.

Hundreds	Tens	Ones

_____

___ + ___ + ___

2.

Hundreds	Tens	Ones

_____

___ + ___ + ___

Hundreds, Tens, and Ones

Write how many hundreds, tens, and ones are
in the model. Write the number in two ways.

1.

Hundreds	Tens	Ones

_____

___ + ___ + ___

2.

Hundreds	Tens	Ones

_____

___ + ___ + ___

3.

Hundreds	Tens	Ones

_____

___ + ___ + ___

Problem Solving

4. Write the number that answers the riddle.
   Use the chart. A model for my number has 6 ones blocks,
   2 hundreds blocks, and 3 tens blocks. What number am I?

Hundreds	Tens	Ones

_____

LESSON 22

Place Value to 1,000

OBJECTIVE Use place value to describe the values of digits in numbers to 1,000.

CC.2.NBT.1

The value of each digit in 426
is shown by its place in the number.

Hundreds	Tens	Ones
4 hundreds	2 tens	6 ones
400	20	6

426

Circle the value or the meaning of the underlined digit.

1. 7<u>8</u>2	800	80	8
2. <u>3</u>52	3 hundreds	3 tens	3 ones
3. 7<u>4</u>2	4	40	400
4. 41<u>9</u>	9 hundreds	9 tens	9 ones
5. <u>5</u>84	500	50	5

CC.2.NBT.1

Place Value to 1,000

Circle the value or the meaning of the underlined digit.

1. 3<u>3</u>7	3	30	300
2. 46<u>2</u>	200	20	2
3. <u>5</u>72	5	50	500
4. 56<u>7</u>	7 ones	7 tens	7 hundreds
5. <u>4</u>62	4 hundreds	4 ones	4 tens
6. <u>1</u>,000	1 ten	1 hundred	1 thousand

Problem Solving

7. Write the 3-digit number that answers the riddle.

- I have the same hundreds digit as my ones digit.
- The value of my tens digit is 50.
- The value of my ones digit is 4.   The number is _____.

LESSON 23

Group Tens as Hundreds

OBJECTIVE Understand that each group of 10 tens is equivalent to 1 hundred.

CC.2.NBT.1a,
CC.2.NBT.1b

There are __10__ ones in this stack.

There are __10__ stacks.

10 stacks of 10 ones is 100 ones.

__10__ tens → __1__ hundred → __100__

Write how many tens. Circle groups of 10 tens.
Write how many hundreds. Write the number.

1.

_____ tens

_____ hundreds

_____ blocks

2.

_____ tens

_____ hundreds

_____ blocks

CC.2.NBT.1a,
CC.2.NBT.1b

Group Tens as Hundreds

Write how many tens. Circle groups of 10 tens.
Write how many hundreds. Write the number.

1.

_____ tens

_____ hundreds

_____ blocks

2.

_____ tens

_____ hundreds

_____ blocks

3.

_____ tens

_____ hundreds

_____ blocks

Problem Solving

Solve. Write or draw to explain.

4. Farmer Gray has 30 flowerpots.
   He planted 10 seeds in each pot.
   How many seeds did he plant?

_____ seeds

LESSON 24
Counting Patterns Within 100

OBJECTIVE Extend counting sequences within 100, counting by 1s, 5s, and 10s.

CC.2.NBT.2

You can count different ways.

Count by fives.

5, 10, 15, 20, 25, 30, 35

Count by tens.

10, 20, 30, 40, 50, 60

Count by fives.

1. 5, 10, 15, 20, _____, _____, _____

2. 20, 25, 30, 35, _____, _____, _____

3. 55, 60, 65, 70, _____, _____, _____

Count by tens.

4. 10, 20, 30, _____, _____, _____

5. 30, 40, 50, 60, _____, _____, _____

CC.2.NBT.2

Counting Patterns Within 100

Count by ones.

1. 58, 59, _____, _____, _____, _____, _____

Count by fives.

2. 45, 50, _____, _____, _____, _____, _____

3. 20, 25, _____, _____, _____, _____, _____

Count by tens.

4. 20, _____, _____, _____, _____, _____, _____

Count back by ones.

5. 87, 86, 85, _____, _____, _____

Problem Solving

6. Tim counts his friends' fingers by fives.
   He counts six hands. What numbers does he say?

   5, _____, _____, _____, _____, _____

© Houghton Mifflin Harcourt Publishing Company

LESSON 25

Counting Patterns Within 1,000

OBJECTIVE Extend counting sequences within 1,000, counting by 1s, 5s, 10s, and 100s.

You can count in different ways.

Look for a pattern to use.

Count by tens.

500, 510, 520, **530, 540, 550**

Count by hundreds.

300, 400, 500, **600, 700, 800**

Count by tens.

1. 410, 420, 430, _____, _____, _____

2. 730, 740, _____, _____, _____

3. 250, 260, _____, _____, _____

Count by hundreds.

4. 100, 200, 300, _____, _____, _____

5. 500, 600, _____, _____, _____

CC.2.NBT.2

Counting Patterns Within 1,000

Count by fives.

1. 415, 420, _____, _____, _____, _____, _____

2. 675, 680, _____, _____, _____, _____, _____

Count by tens.

3. 210, 220, _____, _____, _____, _____, _____

4. 840, 850, _____, _____, _____, _____, _____

Count by hundreds.

5. 300, 400, _____, _____, _____, _____, _____

Count back by ones.

6. 953, 952, _____, _____, _____, _____, _____

Problem Solving

7. Lee has a jar of 100 pennies.
   She adds groups of 10 pennies to the jar.
   She adds 5 groups. What numbers does she say?

   _____, _____, _____, _____, _____

© Houghton Mifflin Harcourt Publishing Company

Name _____

Understand Place Value

OBJECTIVE Use place value to describe the values of digits in 2-digit numbers.

CC.2.NBT.3

0, 1, 2, 3, 4, 5, 6, 7, 8, and 9 are digits.

A digit's place in a number shows the value of the digit.

52 has two digits.

52

The digit __5__ is in the tens place.

The digit 5 shows __5__ tens.

Its value is __50__.

The digit __2__ is in the ones place.

The digit 2 shows __2__ ones.

Its value is __2__.

Circle the value of the underlined digit.

1. <u>2</u>7

20   2

2. <u>1</u>8

10   1   10

3. 5<u>6</u>

60   6

4. <u>3</u>0

30   3

5. 7<u>5</u>

5   50

6. <u>4</u>1

4   40

CC.2.NBT.3

Understand Place Value

Circle the value of the underlined digit.

1. 2̲3

20   2

2. 4̲8

8   80

3. 1̲8

10   1

4. 4̲3

40   4

5. 5̲4

5   50

6. 6̲5

50   5

7. 7̲0

7   70

8. 3̲7

70   7

9. 2̲2

20   2

Problem Solving

Write the 2-digit number that matches the clues.

10. My number has a tens digit that is 8 more than the ones digit. Zero is not one of my digits.

My number is _____.

LESSON 27

Expanded Form

OBJECTIVE Write 2-digit numbers in expanded form.

CC.2.NBT.3

Show tens and ones in 43.

Tens	Ones

```
| | | |        o
               o
               o
```

How many tens? __4__ tens | How many ones? __3__ ones

_43_ is _4_ tens _3_ ones

_43_ is _40_ + _3_

Describe the number in two ways.

1. 35

```
| | |   o
        o
        o
        o
        o
```

____ tens ____ ones

____ + ____

2. 63

```
| | | | | |   o
              o
              o
```

____ tens ____ ones

____ + ____

3. 57

____ tens ____ ones

____ + ____

4. 19

____ ten ____ ones

____ + ____

CC.2.NBT.3

Expanded Form

Draw a quick picture to show the number.
Describe the number in two ways.

1. 68

_____ tens _____ ones

_____ + _____

2. 21

_____ tens _____ one

_____ + _____

3. 70

_____ tens _____ ones

_____ + _____

4. 53

_____ tens _____ ones

_____ + _____

5. 35

_____ tens _____ ones

_____ + _____

6. 47

_____ tens _____ ones

_____ + _____

Problem Solving

7. Circle the ways to write the number shown by the model.

| 4 tens 6 ones | 40 + 6 | 64 |
| 6 tens 4 ones | 60 + 4 | 46 |

LESSON 28 **Different Ways to Write Numbers**

1

CC.2.NBT.3

OBJECTIVE Write 2-digit numbers in word form, expanded form, and standard form.

You can write numbers in different ways.

$$\underline{20} + \underline{6}$$
$$\underline{2} \text{ tens } \underline{6} \text{ ones}$$

twenty-six
$$\underline{26}$$

ones	teen words		tens	
1 one	11 eleven	1 ten 1 one	10 ten	1 ten
2 two	12 twelve	1 ten 2 ones	20 twenty	2 tens
3 three	13 thirteen	1 ten 3 ones	30 thirty	3 tens
4 four	14 fourteen	1 ten 4 ones	40 forty	4 tens
5 five	15 fifteen	1 ten 5 ones	50 fifty	5 tens
6 six	16 sixteen	1 ten 6 ones	60 sixty	6 tens
7 seven	17 seventeen	1 ten 7 ones	70 seventy	7 tens
8 eight	18 eighteen	1 ten 8 ones	80 eighty	8 tens
9 nine	19 nineteen	1 ten 9 ones	90 ninety	9 tens

Write the number another way.

1. twenty

_____

2. 37

_____ tens _____ ones

3. $40 + 5$

_____

4. eighty-one

_____

5. 56

_____

6. 9 tens 2 ones

_____

Different Ways to Write Numbers

Write the number another way.

1. 32

_____ tens _____ ones

2. forty-one

_____

3. 9 tens 5 ones

_____

4. 80 + 3

_____

5. 57

_____ tens _____ ones

6. seventy-two

_____ + _____

7. 60 + 4

_____

8. 4 tens 8 ones

_____

9. twenty-eight

_____ + _____

10. 80

_____ tens _____ ones

Problem Solving

11. A number has the digit 3 in the ones place and the digit 4 in the tens place. Which of these is another way to write this number? Circle it.

3 + 4   40 + 3   30 + 4

LESSON 29

Algebra • Different Names for Numbers

CC.2.NBT.3

OBJECTIVE Apply place value concepts to find equivalent representations of numbers.

Here are some ways to show 28.

Describe the tens and ones with words and addition.

__2__ tens __8__ ones

__20__ + __8__

Describe the tens and ones with words and addition.

__1__ tens __18__ ones

__10__ + __18__

Describe the tens and ones with words and addition.

__0__ tens __28__ ones

__0__ + __28__

Describe the blocks in two ways.

I. 32

_____ tens _____ ones

_____ + _____

_____ tens _____ ones

_____ + _____

_____ tens _____ ones

_____ + _____

CC.2.NBT.3

Algebra • Different Names for Numbers

The blocks show the number in different ways.
Describe the blocks in two ways.

1. 24

_____ tens _____ ones

_____ + _____

_____ tens _____ ones

_____ + _____

_____ tens _____ ones

_____ + _____

2. 36

_____ tens _____ ones

_____ + _____

_____ tens _____ ones

_____ + _____

_____ tens _____ ones

_____ + _____

3. 45

_____ tens _____ ones

_____ + _____

_____ tens _____ ones

_____ + _____

_____ tens _____ ones

_____ + _____

Problem Solving

4. Toni has these blocks. Circle the blocks that she could use to show 34.

LESSON 30 **Problem Solving · Tens and Ones**

OBJECTIVE Solve problems by finding different combinations of tens and ones to represent 2-digit numbers using the strategy *find a pattern*.

CC.2.NBT.3

Anya has 25 toys. She can put them away in boxes of 10 toys or as single toys. What are the different ways Anya can put away the toys?

Unlock the Problem

What do I need to find?

the different
ways

Anya can put away the toys

What information do I need to use?

She can put them away in

boxes of 10 toys or as

single toys.

Look for a pattern.

	2 tens + 5 ones
	1 ten + 15 ones
	0 tens + 25 ones

Boxes of 10 toys	Single toys
2	5
1	15

Find a pattern to solve.

1. Mr. Moore is buying 29 apples. He can buy them in packs of 10 apples or as single apples. What are the different ways Mr. Moore can buy the apples?

Packs of 10 apples	Single apples
2	
1	
0	

Name _____

Problem Solving • Tens and Ones
Find a pattern to solve.

1. Ann is grouping 38 rocks. She can put them into groups of 10 rocks or as single rocks. What are the different ways Ann can group the rocks?

Groups of 10 rocks	Single rocks

2. Mr. Grant needs 30 pieces of felt. He can buy them in packs of 10 or as single pieces. What are the different ways Mr. Grant can buy the felt?

Packs of 10 pieces	Single pieces

3. Ms. Sims is putting away 22 books. She can put them on the table in stacks of 10 or as single books. What are the different ways Ms. Sims can put away the books?

Stacks of 10 books	Single books

© Houghton Mifflin Harcourt Publishing Company

Number Names

OBJECTIVE Read and write 3-digit numbers in word form.

CC.2.NBT.3

You can write a number using words.

257

What is shown with the hundreds blocks?

__two hundred__

What is shown with the tens and ones blocks?

__fifty--seven__

So you write 257 as __two hundred fifty--seven__.

Write the number using words.

1. 163

_____

2. 427

_____

Write the number.

3. two hundred nine

_____

4. five hundred seventy-nine

_____

CC.2.NBT.3

Number Names

Write the number.

1. two hundred thirty-two

_____

2. five hundred forty-four

_____

3. one hundred fifty-eight

_____

4. nine hundred fifty

_____

5. four hundred twenty

_____

6. six hundred seventy-eight

_____

Write the number using words.

7. 317

_____

8. 457

_____

Problem Solving

Circle the answer.

9. Six hundred twenty-six children attend Elm Street School. Which is another way to write this number?

266   626   662

LESSON 32

Different Forms of Numbers

OBJECTIVE Write 3-digit numbers in expanded form and in standard form.

CC.2.NBT.3

There is more than one way to show and write a number.

three hundred sixty-two

_____3_____ hundreds _____6_____ tens _____2_____ ones.

_____300_____ + _____60_____ + _____2_____

_____362_____

Read the number and draw a quick picture.

Then write the number in different ways.

1. four hundred thirty-two

_____ hundreds _____ tens _____ ones

_____ + _____ + _____

_____

---

2. two hundred seventy-five

_____ hundreds _____ tens _____ ones

_____ + _____ + _____

_____

CC.2.NBT.3

Different Forms of Numbers

Read the number and draw a quick picture.
Then write the number in different ways.

1. two hundred fifty-one

_____ hundreds _____ tens _____ ones

_____ + _____ + _____

_____

---

2. three hundred twelve

_____ hundreds _____ tens _____ ones

_____ + _____ + _____

---

3. two hundred seven

_____ hundreds _____ tens _____ ones

_____ + _____ + _____

_____

Problem Solving

Write the number another way.

4. $200 + 30 + 7$

_____

5. 895

_____

© Houghton Mifflin Harcourt Publishing Company

LESSON 33

Algebra • Different Ways to Show Numbers

CC.2.NBT.3

OBJECTIVE Apply place value concepts to find equivalent representations of numbers.

These two models can both be used to show the number 124.

I ten has the same value as 10 ones.

Hundreds	Tens	Ones
1	2	4

Hundreds	Tens	Ones
1	1	14

Write how many hundreds, tens, and ones are in the model.

1. 132

Hundreds	Tens	Ones

Hundreds	Tens	Ones

2. 246

Hundreds	Tens	Ones

Hundreds	Tens	Ones

Algebra • Different Ways to Show Numbers

Write how many hundreds, tens, and ones are in the model.

1. 135

Hundreds	Tens	Ones

Hundreds	Tens	Ones

2. 216

Hundreds	Tens	Ones

Hundreds	Tens	Ones

Problem Solving

Markers are sold in boxes, packs, or as single markers.
Each box has 10 packs. Each pack has 10 markers.

3. Draw pictures to show two ways
to buy 276 markers.

LESSON 34

Problem Solving • Compare Numbers

OBJECTIVE Solve problems involving number comparisons by using the strategy *make a model.*

At the zoo, there are 137 birds and 142 reptiles.

Are there more birds or more reptiles at the zoo?

Unlock the Problem

What do I need to find?	**What information do I need to use?**
I need to find if there are more __**birds**__ or __**reptiles**__.	There are __137__ birds. There are __142__ reptiles.

Show how to solve the problem.

Birds   Reptiles

The number of hundreds is the same.

There are more tens in the number of reptiles.

So, there are more __**reptiles**__ at the zoo.

Draw quick pictures to model the numbers.

1. There are 153 birds and 149 fish at the nature center.
   Are there more birds or more fish?

   There are more _____.

Problem Solving • Compare Numbers

**Model the numbers. Draw quick pictures
to show how you solved the problem.**

1. Lauryn has 128 marbles. Kristin has
    118 marbles. Who has more marbles?

    _____

2. Nick has 189 trading cards. Kyle has
    198 trading cards. Who has fewer
    cards?

    _____

3. A piano has 36 black keys and 52 white
    keys. Are there more black keys or white
    keys on a piano?

    _____

4. There are 253 cookies in a bag. There
    are 266 cookies in a box. Are there
    fewer cookies in the bag or in the box?

    _____

LESSON 35

Algebra · Compare Numbers

OBJECTIVE Compare 3-digit numbers using the >, =, and < symbols.

 1 CC.2.NBT.4

To compare 3-digit numbers, first compare hundreds.

2̲12 has more hundreds than 1̲12.

212 (>>) 112

If hundreds are equal, then compare tens.

21̲2 has fewer tens than 22̲1.

212 (<) 221

If hundreds and tens are equal, then compare ones.

212 (⋯) 212

Compare the numbers. Write >, <, or =.

I.   317   ◯   326

2.   582   ◯   634

CC.2.NBT.4

Algebra • Compare Numbers

Compare the numbers. Write >, <, or =.

1. 489
605

489 ◯ 605

2. 719
719

719 ◯ 719

3. 370
248

370 ◯ 248

4. 645
654

645 ◯ 654

5. 205
250

205 ◯ 250

6. 813
781

813 ◯ 781

7. 397
393

397 ◯ 393

8. 504
405

504 ◯ 405

Problem Solving

Solve. Write or draw to explain.

9. Toby has 178 pennies.
Bella has 190 pennies.
Who has more pennies?

_____ has more pennies.

LESSON 36 **2-Digit Addition**

OBJECTIVE Record 2-digit addition using the standard algorithm.

CC.2.NBT.5

Add 27 and 36.

STEP 1	**STEP 2**	**STEP 3**
Model 27 and 36. Add the ones. $7 + 6 = 13$	If you can make a 10, regroup 10 ones for 1 ten. 13 ones = 1 ten 3 ones	Add the tens. Remember to add the regrouped ten. $1 + 2 + 3 = 6$

STEP 1

Tens	Ones

	Tens	Ones
	2	7
+	3	6

STEP 2

Tens	Ones

	Tens	Ones
	2	7
+	3	6
		3

STEP 3

Tens	Ones

	Tens	Ones
	1	
	2	7
+	3	6
	6	3

Regroup if you need to. Write the sum.

1.

Tens	Ones
5	4
+ 2	9

2.

Tens	Ones
1	7
+ 6	1

3.

Tens	Ones
4	1
+ 2	9

4.

Tens	Ones
3	5
+ 3	2

CC.2.NBT.5

2-Digit Addition

Regroup if you need to. Write the sum.

1.
$$\begin{array}{c|c} 4 & 7 \\ +2 & 5 \\ \hline \end{array}$$

2.
$$\begin{array}{c|c} 3 & 3 \\ +1 & 8 \\ \hline \end{array}$$

3.
$$\begin{array}{c|c} 2 & 8 \\ +6 & 4 \\ \hline \end{array}$$

4.
$$\begin{array}{c|c} 1 & 3 \\ +6 & 5 \\ \hline \end{array}$$

5.
$$\begin{array}{c|c} 1 & 7 \\ +2 & 6 \\ \hline \end{array}$$

6.
$$\begin{array}{c|c} 3 & 6 \\ +5 & 3 \\ \hline \end{array}$$

7.
$$\begin{array}{c|c} 5 & 8 \\ +2 & 5 \\ \hline \end{array}$$

8.
$$\begin{array}{c|c} 3 & 7 \\ +4 & 9 \\ \hline \end{array}$$

9.
$$\begin{array}{c|c} 5 & 2 \\ +2 & 9 \\ \hline \end{array}$$

10.
$$\begin{array}{c|c} 6 & 6 \\ +2 & 4 \\ \hline \end{array}$$

11.
$$\begin{array}{c|c} 7 & 4 \\ +1 & 4 \\ \hline \end{array}$$

12.
$$\begin{array}{c|c} 3 & 7 \\ +3 & 7 \\ \hline \end{array}$$

Problem Solving

Solve. Write or draw to explain.

13. Angela drew 16 flowers on her paper in the morning. She drew 25 more flowers in the afternoon. How many flowers did she draw in all?

_____ flowers

Practice 2-Digit Addition

OBJECTIVE Practice 2-digit addition with and without regrouping.

CC.2.NBT.5

Eliza sold 47 pencils in one week.

She sold 65 pencils the next week.

How many pencils did she sell in both weeks?

Add 47 and 65. Add the ones.	Regroup.	Add the tens.
$7 + 5 = 12$	12 ones = 1 ten and 2 ones	$1 + 4 + 6 = 11$

Write the sum.

I.

```
  4 3
+ 6 9
```

2.

```
  7 6
+ 5 8
```

3.

```
  3 8
+ 4 2
```

4.

```
  8 5
+ 6 8
```

5.

```
  8 2
+ 4 7
```

6.

```
  8 1
+ 1 7
```

7.

```
  2 7
+ 8 6
```

8.

```
  5 1
+ 3 8
```

Practice 2-Digit Addition

Write the sum.

1.

$$\begin{array}{r} 58 \\ +17 \\ \hline \end{array}$$

2.

$$\begin{array}{r} 44 \\ +86 \\ \hline \end{array}$$

3.

$$\begin{array}{r} 36 \\ +13 \\ \hline \end{array}$$

4.

$$\begin{array}{r} 49 \\ +72 \\ \hline \end{array}$$

5.

$$\begin{array}{r} 58 \\ +87 \\ \hline \end{array}$$

6.

$$\begin{array}{r} 32 \\ +59 \\ \hline \end{array}$$

7.

$$\begin{array}{r} 77 \\ +58 \\ \hline \end{array}$$

8.

$$\begin{array}{r} 45 \\ +45 \\ \hline \end{array}$$

9.

$$\begin{array}{r} 54 \\ +28 \\ \hline \end{array}$$

Problem Solving

Solve. Write or draw to explain.

10. There are 45 books on the shelf.
There are 37 books on the table.
How many books in all are on the
shelf and the table?

_____ books

LESSON 38

Rewrite 2-Digit Addition

OBJECTIVE Rewrite horizontal addition problems vertically in the standard algorithm format.

CC.2.NBT.5

Add. 43 + 19 = ?

STEP 1	STEP 2	STEP 3
What is the tens digit in 43? __4__ Write 4 in the tens column. Write the ones digit, 3, in the ones column.	What is the tens digit in 19? __1__ Write 1 in the tens column. Write the ones digit, 9, in the ones column.	Add the ones. Regroup if you need to. Add the tens.

Tens	Ones
4	3
+	

Tens	Ones
4	3
+ 1	9

Tens	Ones
4	3
+ 1	9
6	2

Rewrite the numbers. Then add.

1. 26 + 9

2. 16 + 43

3. 32 + 38

4. 23 + 26

Rewrite 2-Digit Addition

Rewrite the numbers. Then add.

1. 27 + 19

+ _____

2. 36 + 23

+ _____

3. 31 + 29

+ _____

4. 48 + 23

+ _____

5. 53 + 12

+ _____

6. 69 + 13

+ _____

7. 24 + 38

+ _____

8. 46 + 37

+ _____

Problem Solving

Use the table. Show how you solved the problem.

9. How many pages in all did Sasha and Kara read?

Pages Read This Week	
Child	Number of Pages
Sasha	62
Kara	29
Juan	50

_____ pages

LESSON 39

Algebra · Break Apart Ones to Subtract

CC.2.NBT.5

OBJECTIVE Break apart a 1-digit subtrahend to subtract it from a 2-digit number.

To subtract a one-digit number,
break it apart.

Break apart ones in 7.

- Use 4 because 44 has
  a 4 in the ones place.

- The other part is 3.

$44 - 7 =$ ___?___

Start at 44.
Subtract 4, and then subtract 3.

-3 -4

30 31 32 33 34 35 36 37 38 39 **40** 41 42 43 44 45 46 47 48 49 **50**

So, $44 - 7 =$ __37__.

Break apart ones to subtract. Write the difference.

30 31 32 33 34 35 36 37 38 39 **40** 41 42 43 44 45 46 47 48 49 **50**

1. $42 - 8 =$ _____

2. $47 - 8 =$ _____

3. $43 - 5 =$ _____

4. $41 - 8 =$ _____

Algebra • Break Apart Ones to Subtract

Break apart ones to subtract. Write the difference.

20 21 22 23 24 25 26 27 28 29 **30** 31 32 33 34 35 36 37 38 39 **40** 41 42 43 44 45 46 47 48 49 **50**

1. $36 - 7 =$ _____

2. $35 - 8 =$ _____

3. $37 - 9 =$ _____

4. $41 - 6 =$ _____

5. $44 - 5 =$ _____

6. $33 - 7 =$ _____

7. $32 - 4 =$ _____

8. $31 - 6 =$ _____

9. $46 - 9 =$ _____

10. $43 - 5 =$ _____

Problem Solving

Choose a way to solve. Write or draw to explain.

11. Beth had 44 marbles. She gave
9 marbles to her brother.
How many marbles does
Beth have now?

_____ marbles

LESSON 40 # Algebra • Break Apart Numbers to Subtract

CC.2.NBT.5

OBJECTIVE Break apart a 2-digit subtrahend to subtract it from a 2-digit number.

To subtract a two-digit number, break it apart.

First, break apart 16 into tens and ones.

Now, break apart the ones in 6.

- Use 4 because 54 has a 4 in the ones place.

- The other part is 2.

Use the number line to subtract the three parts.

$$54 - 16 = \underline{\ ?\ }$$

10   6

4   2

−2   −4   −10

35 36 37 38 39 40 41 42 43 44 45 46 47 48 49 50 51 52 53 54 55

So, $54 - 16 = \underline{38}$.

Break apart the number you are subtracting.
Write the difference.

30 31 32 33 34 35 36 37 38 39 40 41 42 43 44 45 46 47 48 49 50 51 52 53 54 55 56 57 58 59 60

I. $51 - 16 = \underline{\hspace{1cm}}$

2. $57 - 18 = \underline{\hspace{1cm}}$

3. $54 - 17 = \underline{\hspace{1cm}}$

4. $52 - 18 = \underline{\hspace{1cm}}$

CC.2.NBT.5

Algebra · Break Apart Numbers to Subtract

Break apart the number you are subtracting. Write the difference.

| 60 | 61 | 62 | 63 | 64 | 65 | 66 | 67 | 68 | 69 | **70** | 71 | 72 | 73 | 74 | 75 | 76 | 77 | 78 | 79 | **80** | 81 | 82 | 83 | 84 | 85 | 86 | 87 | 88 | 89 | **90** |

1. $81 - 14 =$ _____

2. $84 - 16 =$ _____

3. $77 - 14 =$ _____

4. $83 - 19 =$ _____

5. $81 - 17 =$ _____

6. $88 - 13 =$ _____

7. $84 - 19 =$ _____

8. $86 - 18 =$ _____

9. $84 - 17 =$ _____

10. $76 - 15 =$ _____

11. $86 - 12 =$ _____

12. $82 - 19 =$ _____

Problem Solving

Solve. Write or draw to explain.

13. Mr. Pearce bought 43 plants. He gave
14 plants to his sister. How many
plants does Mr. Pearce have now?

_____ plants

Model and Record 2-Digit Subtraction

OBJECTIVE Draw quick pictures and record 2-digit subtraction using the standard algorithm.

CC.2.NBT.5

		Tens	Ones		Tens	Ones
Subtract. 54 − 15 Are there enough ones to subtract 5? **no**		‖‖‖‖‖	∘ ∘ ∘ ∘		5 − 1	4 5

		Tens	Ones		Tens	Ones
Regroup 1 ten as 10 ones. Write the new number of tens and ones.		‖‖‖‖	∘∘∘ ∘∘∘ ∘∘∘ ∘∘∘		4 14 5̶ 4̶ − 1 5	

		Tens	Ones		Tens	Ones
Subtract the ones. 14 ones − 5 ones = **9** ones Write that number in the ones place. Subtract the tens. 4 tens − 1 ten = **3** tens Write that number in the tens place.		‖‖‖	∘∘ ∘∘ ∘∘		4 14 5̶ 4̶ − 1 5 3 9	

Draw a quick picture to solve. Write the difference.

1.

Tens	Ones
☐	☐
4	3
− 1	6

Tens	Ones

2.

Tens	Ones
☐	☐
3	1
− 1	7

Tens	Ones

CC.2.NBT.5

Model and Record 2-Digit Subtraction

Draw a quick picture to solve.

Write the difference.

1.

Tens	Ones
☐	☐
4	3
− 1	7

Tens	Ones

2.

Tens	Ones
☐	☐
3	8
− 2	9

Tens	Ones

3.

Tens	Ones
☐	☐
5	2
− 3	7

Tens	Ones

4.

Tens	Ones
☐	☐
3	5
− 1	9

Tens	Ones

Problem Solving

Solve. Write or draw to explain.

5. Kendall has 63 stickers.
Her sister has 57 stickers.
How many more stickers does
Kendall have than her sister?

_____ more stickers

2-Digit Subtraction

OBJECTIVE Record 2-digit subtraction using the standard algorithm.

CC.2.NBT.5

Subtract.   54
               − 28

Are there enough

ones to subtract 8? __no__

Tens	Ones
5	4
− 2	8

Regroup 1 ten as 10 ones.

Write the new number
of tens and ones.

Tens	Ones
4	14
5̷	4̷
− 2	8

Subtract the ones.

14 ones − 8 ones = __6__ ones

Write that number in the ones place.

Tens	Ones
4	14
5̷	4̷
− 2	8
	6

Subtract the tens.

4 tens − 2 tens = __2__ tens

Write that number in the tens place.

Tens	Ones
4	14
5̷	4̷
− 2	8
2	6

Regroup if you need to. Write the difference.

1.

Tens	Ones
7	2
− 4	5

2.

Tens	Ones
5	1
− 1	3

3.

Tens	Ones
3	8
− 1	6

2-Digit Subtraction

Regroup if you need to.
Write the difference.

1.

Tens	Ones
☐	☐

$$\begin{array}{c} 4 \;\;\; 7 \\ -2 \;\;\; 8 \\ \hline \end{array}$$

2.

Tens	Ones
☐	☐

$$\begin{array}{c} 3 \;\;\; 3 \\ -1 \;\;\; 8 \\ \hline \end{array}$$

3.

Tens	Ones
☐	☐

$$\begin{array}{c} 2 \;\;\; 8 \\ -1 \;\;\; 4 \\ \hline \end{array}$$

4.

Tens	Ones
☐	☐

$$\begin{array}{c} 6 \;\;\; 6 \\ -1 \;\;\; 9 \\ \hline \end{array}$$

5.

$$\begin{array}{c} 7 \;\;\; 7 \\ -2 \;\;\; 6 \\ \hline \end{array}$$

6.

$$\begin{array}{c} 5 \;\;\; 8 \\ -3 \;\;\; 4 \\ \hline \end{array}$$

7.

$$\begin{array}{c} 5 \;\;\; 2 \\ -2 \;\;\; 5 \\ \hline \end{array}$$

8.

$$\begin{array}{c} 8 \;\;\; 7 \\ -4 \;\;\; 9 \\ \hline \end{array}$$

Problem Solving

Solve. Write or draw to explain.

9. Mrs. Paul bought 32 erasers. She gave
19 erasers to students. How many erasers
does she still have?

_____ erasers

LESSON 43

Practice 2-Digit Subtraction

OBJECTIVE Practice 2-digit subtraction with and without regrouping.

Clay scored 80 points. Meg scored 61 points.
How many more points did Clay score than Meg?

STEP 1	STEP 2	STEP 3
More ones are needed. Regroup 8 tens 0 ones as 7 tens 10 ones.	Subtract in the ones column.	Subtract in the tens column.

STEP 1
```
  7  10
  8   0
- 6   1
```

STEP 2
```
  7  10
  8   0
- 6   1
      9
```

STEP 3
```
  7  10
  8   0
- 6   1
  1   9
```

Write the difference.

1.
```
  6 0
- 2 7
```

2.
```
  3 7
- 2 2
```

3.
```
  6 1
- 4 8
```

4.
```
  7 0
- 2 6
```

5.
```
  3 7
- 1 9
```

6.
```
  5 5
- 1 4
```

CC.2.NBT.5

Practice 2-Digit Subtraction

Write the difference.

1.
```
   5 0
 - 1 8
```

2.
```
   4 3
 - 1 7
```

3.
```
   7 5
 - 1 8
```

4.
```
   2 2
 -   6
```

5.
```
   6 0
 - 3 5
```

6.
```
   4 2
 - 3 4
```

7.
```
   2 1
 -   8
```

8.
```
   3 9
 - 2 7
```

9.
```
   6 1
 - 3 7
```

Problem Solving

Solve. Write or draw to explain.

10. Julie has 42 sheets of paper.
She gives 17 sheets to Kari.
How many sheets of paper
does Julie have now?

_____ sheets of paper

© Houghton Mifflin Harcourt Publishing Company

Name _____

LESSON 44

Rewrite 2-Digit Subtraction

OBJECTIVE Rewrite horizontal subtraction problems vertically in the standard algorithm format.

CC.2.NBT.5

62 − 38 = ?

Rewrite 62 first.

62

The 6 is in the tens place. Write it in the tens column.

The 2 is in the ones place. Write it in the ones column.

Tens	Ones
☐ 6	☐ 2
−	

Then rewrite 38.

38

The 3 is in the tens place. Write it in the tens column.

The 8 is in the ones place. Write it in the ones column.

Tens	Ones
☐ 6	☐ 2
− 3	8

Now the ones digits are in a column and the tens digits are in a column.

Subtract. Write the difference.

Tens	Ones
5 6	12 2
− 3	8
2	4

Rewrite the subtraction problem. Find the difference.

1. 56 − 24

Tens	Ones
☐	☐
−	

2. 74 − 37

Tens	Ones
☐	☐
−	

3. 43 − 15

Tens	Ones
☐	☐
−	

© Houghton Mifflin Harcourt Publishing Company

CC.2.NBT.5

Rewrite 2-Digit Subtraction

Rewrite the subtraction problem.
Then find the difference.

1. $35 - 19$

_____
_____

2. $47 - 23$

_____
_____

3. $55 - 28$

_____
_____

4. $22 - 15$

_____
_____

5. $61 - 32$

_____
_____

6. $70 - 37$

_____
_____

Problem Solving

Solve. Write or draw to explain.

7. Jimmy went to the toy store. He saw
23 wooden trains and 41 plastic trains.
How many more plastic trains than
wooden trains did he see?

_____ more plastic trains

LESSON 45

Add to Find Differences

OBJECTIVE Use addition to find differences.

 CC.2.NBT.5

Count up to solve. $34 - 27 = ?$
Start at 27. Count up 3 to 30.

To get to 34 from 30, count up 4 more.

7 was added to get to 34.

So, $34 - 27 = \underline{7}$.

Count up to find the difference.

1. $41 - 37 = \underline{}$

2. $43 - 38 = \underline{}$

CC.2.NBT.5

Add to Find Differences

Use the number line. Count up
to find the difference.

1. 36 − 29 = _____

20 21 22 23 24 25 26 27 28 29 **30** 31 32 33 34 35 36 37 38 39 **40**

2. 43 − 35 = _____

30 31 32 33 34 35 36 37 38 39 **40** 41 42 43 44 45 46 47 48 49 **50**

3. 76 − 68 = _____

60 61 62 63 64 65 66 67 68 69 **70** 71 72 73 74 75 76 77 78 79 **80**

Problem Solving

Solve. You may wish to use the number line.

50 51 52 53 54 55 56 57 58 59 **60** 61 62 63 64 65 66 67 68 69 **70**

4. Jill has 63 index cards. She uses
57 of them for a project. How many
index cards does Jill have now?

_____ index cards

Lesson 45

LESSON 46 | Break Apart Ones to Add

OBJECTIVE Find a sum by breaking apart a 1-digit addend to make a 2-digit addend a multiple of 10.

CC.2.NBT.6

Sometimes when you are adding, you can break apart ones to make a ten.

$37 + 8 = \underline{?}$

Look at the two-digit addend, 37. What digit

is in the ones place? __7__

Decide how many you need to add to the ones digit to make 10.

$7 + \underline{3} = 10$, and $37 + \underline{3} = \textbf{40}$

Break apart that number from the one-digit addend, 8.

$8 - 3 = \textbf{5}$

Finally, write the new number sentence. $40 + 5 = \underline{45}$

Break apart ones to make a ten.
Then add and write the sum.

1. $28 + 6 = $ _____

2. $34 + 7 = $ _____

Break Apart Ones to Add

Break apart ones to make a ten.
Then add and write the sum.

1. 62 + 9 = _____

2. 27 + 7 = _____

3. 28 + 5 = _____

4. 17 + 8 = _____

5. 57 + 6 = _____

6. 23 + 9 = _____

7. 39 + 7 = _____

8. 26 + 5 = _____

9. 13 + 8 = _____

10. 18 + 7 = _____

11. 49 + 8 = _____

12. 27 + 5 = _____

13. 39 + 4 = _____

14. 18 + 8 = _____

Problem Solving

Solve. Write or draw to explain.

15. Jimmy had 18 toy airplanes. His mother
bought him 7 more toy airplanes. How many
toy airplanes does he have now?

_____ toy airplanes

LESSON 47 **Use Compensation**

OBJECTIVE Use compensation to develop flexible thinking for 2-digit addition.

CC.2.NBT.6

This is a way to add 2-digit numbers.
Take ones from one addend to make the other addend a tens number.

$27 + 38 = \underline{?}$

First, find the addend with the greater ones digit. $\underline{38}$
How many ones would you need to add to make it a tens number?

$\left(38 + \underline{} = 40 \right)$ Add $\underline{2}$ to make $\underline{40}$.

Next, take that many ones away from the other addend.

$\left(27 - 2 = 25 \right)$ The two new addends are $\underline{25}$ and $\underline{40}$.

Write the new addition sentence to find the sum.

$\underline{25} + \underline{40} = \underline{65}$

Show how to make one addend the next tens number.
Complete the new addition sentence.

1. $28 + 16 = ?$

$\underline{} + \underline{} = \underline{}$

2. $37 + 24 = ?$

$\underline{} + \underline{} = \underline{}$

Use Compensation

Show how to make one addend the next tens number.
Complete the new addition sentence.

1. $15 + 37 = ?$

_____ + _____ = _____

2. $22 + 49 = ?$

_____ + _____ = _____

3. $38 + 26 = ?$

_____ + _____ = _____

4. $27 + 47 = ?$

_____ + _____ = _____

Problem Solving

Solve. Write or draw to explain.

5. The oak tree at the school was 34 feet tall.
Then it grew 18 feet taller.
How tall is the oak tree now?

_____ feet tall

LESSON 48

Break Apart Addends as Tens and Ones

OBJECTIVE Apply place-value concepts when using a break-apart strategy for 2-digit addition.

$25 + 46 = ?$

Break apart 25 into tens and ones.   Break apart 46 into tens and ones.

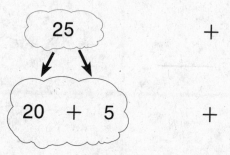

Then, add the tens from the two addends. $\underline{20} + \underline{40} = \underline{60}$

Add the ones from the two addends. $\underline{5} + \underline{6} = \underline{11}$

Add the two sums. $\underline{60} + \underline{11} = \underline{71}$

So, $25 + 46 = \underline{71}$.

Break apart the addends to find the sum.

1.   12   +   48 = ?

_____ + _____ + _____ + _____

Add the tens.   _____ + _____ = _____

Add the ones.   _____ + _____ = _____

How many?   _____ + _____ = _____

So, $12 + 48 =$ _____.

CC.2.NBT.6

Break Apart Addends as Tens and Ones

Break apart the addends to find the sum.

1. 18 → ____ + ____

   + 21 → ____ + ____
   _____

   ____ + ____ = ____

2. 33 → ____ + ____

   + 49 → ____ + ____

   ____ + ____ = ____

3. 72 → ____ + ____

   + 18 → ____ + ____

   ____ + ____ = ____

Problem Solving

Choose a way to solve.
Write or draw to explain.

4. Christopher has 28 baseball cards.
   Justin has 18 baseball cards. How
   many baseball cards do they
   have?

   _____ baseball cards

LESSON 49

Model and Record 2-Digit Addition

OBJECTIVE Draw quick pictures and record 2-digit addition using the standard algorithm.

Model 33 + 19.

How many ones are there in all? __12__ ones

Can you make a ten? __yes__

Tens	Ones

Tens	Ones
☐	
3	3
+ 1	9

Regroup 10 ones as 1 ten. Write a 1 in the tens column to show the regrouped ten.

How many ones are left after regrouping? __2__ ones

Write that number in the ones place.

Tens	Ones

Tens	Ones
☐	
3	3
+ 1	9
	2

How many tens are there in all? __5__ tens

Write that number in the tens place.

Tens	Ones

Tens	Ones
1	
3	3
+ 1	9
5	2

Draw quick pictures to help you solve. Write the sum.

1.

Tens	Ones
☐	
4	7
+ 2	5

Tens	Ones

2.

Tens	Ones
☐	
3	6
+ 4	6

Tens	Ones

Model and Record 2-Digit Addition

Draw quick pictures to help you solve.
Write the sum.

1.

Tens	Ones
☐	
3	8
+ 1	7

Tens	Ones

2.

Tens	Ones
☐	
5	8
+ 2	6

Tens	Ones

3.

Tens	Ones
☐	
4	2
+ 3	7

Tens	Ones

4.

Tens	Ones
☐	
5	3
+ 3	8

Tens	Ones

Problem Solving

Choose a way to solve.
Write or draw to explain.

5. There were 37 children at the park on
Saturday and 25 children at the park
on Sunday. How many children were
at the park on those two days? _____ children

Algebra • Find Sums for 3 Addends

OBJECTIVE Find sums of three 2-digit numbers.

CC.2.NBT.6

You can add three numbers in different ways.
Start by adding the ones first.

14
22
+36
72

Look at the column of ones digits. Choose two of the digits to add first. Then add the other digit.

$$4 + 6 = 10$$
$$10 + 2 = 12$$

Then add the tens.

$$1 + 1 + 2 + 3 = 7$$

14
22
+36
72

Start at the top of the ones column. Add the first two digits, and then add the third digit.

$$4 + 2 = 6$$
$$6 + 6 = 12$$

Then add the tens.

$$1 + 1 + 2 + 3 = 7$$

So, $14 + 22 + 36 = 72$.

Add.

1.	**2.**	**3.**	**4.**
18	40	13	26
25	37	21	22
+32	+16	+34	+23

Algebra • Find Sums for 3 Addends

Add.

1.
$$\begin{array}{r} 23 \\ 20 \\ +25 \\ \hline \end{array}$$

2.
$$\begin{array}{r} 15 \\ 22 \\ +38 \\ \hline \end{array}$$

3.
$$\begin{array}{r} 13 \\ 52 \\ +34 \\ \hline \end{array}$$

4.
$$\begin{array}{r} 27 \\ 40 \\ +19 \\ \hline \end{array}$$

5.
$$\begin{array}{r} 31 \\ 45 \\ +24 \\ \hline \end{array}$$

6.
$$\begin{array}{r} 34 \\ 11 \\ +28 \\ \hline \end{array}$$

7.
$$\begin{array}{r} 42 \\ 36 \\ +11 \\ \hline \end{array}$$

8.
$$\begin{array}{r} 18 \\ 22 \\ +34 \\ \hline \end{array}$$

9.
$$\begin{array}{r} 53 \\ 19 \\ +25 \\ \hline \end{array}$$

Problem Solving

Solve. Write or draw to explain.

10. Liam has 24 yellow pencils,
15 red pencils, and 9 blue pencils.
How many pencils does he have
altogether?

_____ pencils

Algebra · Find Sums for 4 Addends

OBJECTIVE Find sums of four 2-digit numbers.

You can add 4 numbers in different ways.
One way is to add pairs of digits in the ones column.

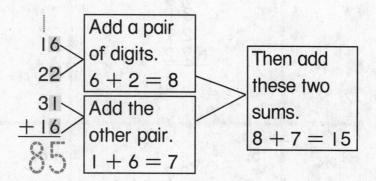

Then add the digits in the tens column.

So, $16 + 22 + 31 + 16 = 85$.

Add.

1.
```
   43
   57
   32
 +  2
```

2.
```
   24
   21
   19
 + 32
```

3.
```
   21
   14
   20
 + 42
```

CC.2.NBT.6

Algebra • Find Sums for 4 Addends

Add.

1.

```
  1 8
  3 2
  2 3
+   3
```

2.

```
  4 5
  3 1
  2 9
+ 7 2
```

3.

```
  2 4
  6 2
  7 0
+ 3 3
```

4.

```
  8 3
  3 2
  6 1
+ 2 2
```

5.

```
  3 7
  1 5
  3 1
+ 1 2
```

6.

```
  2 1
  1 3
  9 6
+ 1 8
```

Problem Solving

Solve. Show how you solved the problem.

7. Kinza jogs 16 minutes on Monday, 13 minutes on Tuesday, 9 minutes on Wednesday, and 20 minutes on Thursday. What is the total number of minutes she jogged?

_____ minutes

Draw to Represent 3-Digit Addition

OBJECTIVE Draw quick pictures to represent 3-digit addition.

CC.2.NBT.7

Add 213 and 124.
Draw quick pictures of 213 and 124.

Count the hundreds, tens, and ones.

_3_ hundreds _3_ tens _7_ ones

Write the number. _337_

Hundreds	Tens	Ones
☐ ☐ ☐	l	○ ○ ○
☐	ll	○ ○ ○ ○

Draw quick pictures. Write how many hundreds, tens, and ones. Write the number.

1. Add 135 and 214.

Hundreds	Tens	Ones
☐	llll	○ ○ ○ ○ ○

_____ hundreds _____ tens _____ ones

_____

2. Add 121 and 143.

Hundreds	Tens	Ones

_____ hundreds _____ tens _____ ones

_____

CC.2.NBT.7

Draw to Represent 3-Digit Addition

Draw quick pictures. Write how many hundreds,
tens, and ones. Write the number.

1. Add 142 and 215.

Hundreds	Tens	Ones

_____ hundreds _____ tens _____ ones

_____

2. Add 263 and 206.

Hundreds	Tens	Ones

_____ hundreds _____ tens _____ ones

_____

Problem Solving

Solve. Write or draw to explain.

3. A farmer sold 324 lemons and 255 limes.
How many pieces of fruit did the farmer
sell altogether?

_____ pieces of fruit

LESSON 53

Break Apart 3-Digit Addends

OBJECTIVE Apply place value concepts when using a break apart strategy for 3-digit addition.

CC.2.NBT.7

743
+124

Break apart each addend.
Write the value of each digit.

$743 = \underline{700} + \underline{40} + \underline{3}$

$124 = \underline{100} + \underline{20} + \underline{4}$

Add the hundreds, tens, and ones.
Then add these sums together.

Hundreds	**Tens**	**Ones**

743 ⟶ 700 + 40 + 3

+124 ⟶ 100 + 20 + 4

800 + 60 + 7 = 867

Break apart the addends to find the sum.

Hundreds	**Tens**	**Ones**

I.   253 ⟶ ____ + ____ + ____

+536 ⟶ ____ + ____ + ____

____ + ____ + ____ = ____

CC.2.NBT.7

Break Apart 3-Digit Addends

Break apart the addends to find the sum.

1. 518 ⟶ ___ + ___ + ___

    +221 ⟶ ___ + ___ + ___

    ___ + ___ + ___ = ___

2. 438 ⟶ ___ + ___ + ___

    +142 ⟶ ___ + ___ + ___

    ___ + ___ + ___ = ___

3. 324 ⟶ ___ + ___ + ___

    +239 ⟶ ___ + ___ + ___

    ___ + ___ + ___ = ___

Problem Solving

Solve. Write or draw to explain.

4. There are 126 crayons in a bucket.
    A teacher puts 144 more crayons
    in the bucket. How many crayons
    are in the bucket now?

    _____ crayons

LESSON 54

3-Digit Addition: Regroup Ones

OBJECTIVE Record 3-digit addition using the standard algorithm with possible regrouping of ones.

CC.2.NBT.7

Add.   318
      +256

Hundreds	Tens	Ones

Hundreds	Tens	Ones
3	1	8
+ 2	5	6

Add the ones.

$8 + 6 =$ __14__

Do you need to regroup? __yes__

Regroup 10 ones as 1 ten.

Hundreds	Tens	Ones
	1	
3	1	8
+ 2	5	6
		4

Add the tens.

$1 + 1 + 5 =$ __7__

Add the hundreds.

$3 + 2 =$ __5__

So, $318 + 256 = 574.$

Hundreds	Tens	Ones
	1	
3	1	8
+ 2	5	6
5	7	4

Write the sum.

1.

Hundreds	Tens	Ones
5	2	6
+ 1	4	2

2.

Hundreds	Tens	Ones
4	5	7
+ 3	3	5

CC.2.NBT.7

3-Digit Addition: Regroup Ones

Write the sum.

1.

Hundreds	Tens	Ones
	☐	
1	4	8
+ 2	3	4

2.

Hundreds	Tens	Ones
	☐	
3	2	1
+ 3	1	8

3.

Hundreds	Tens	Ones
	☐	
4	1	4
+ 1	7	9

4.

Hundreds	Tens	Ones
	☐	
6	0	2
+ 2	5	8

Problem Solving

Solve. Write or draw to explain.

5. In the garden, there are 258 yellow daisies and 135 white daisies. How many daisies are in the garden altogether?

_____ daisies

LESSON 55

3-Digit Addition: Regroup Tens

OBJECTIVE Record 3-digit addition using the standard algorithm with possible regrouping of tens.

Add.   271
      + 158

Add the ones.

$1 + 8 =$ ___9___

Hundreds	Tens	Ones
2	7	1
+ 1	5	8
		9

Add the tens.

$7 + 5 =$ ___12___

Do you need to regroup? ___yes___

Regroup 12 tens as 1 hundred 2 tens.

Hundreds	Tens	Ones
1		
2	7	1
+ 1	5	8
	2	9

Add the hundreds.

$1 + 2 + 1 =$ ___4___

Hundreds	Tens	Ones
1		
2	7	1
+ 1	5	8
4	2	9

Write the sum.

1.

Hundreds	Tens	Ones
2	6	4
+ 1	4	5

2.

Hundreds	Tens	Ones
2	3	2
+ 6	0	6

Name _____

CC.2.NBT.7

3-Digit Addition: Regroup Tens

Write the sum.

1.

Hundreds	Tens	Ones
□	□	
1	8	7
+ 2	3	2

2.

Hundreds	Tens	Ones
□	□	
3	2	2
+ 3	5	6

3.

Hundreds	Tens	Ones
□	□	
2	8	5
+ 5	3	1

4.
```
  4 4 5
+   3 4
```

5.
```
  6 2 0
+ 2 8 8
```

6.
```
  5 5 7
+ 1 8 0
```

7.
```
  6 7 1
+ 1 5 4
```

8.
```
  4 6 3
+ 4 8 1
```

9.
```
  7 4 6
+ 1 3 3
```

Problem Solving

Solve. Write or draw to explain.

10. There are 142 blue toy cars and 293 red toy cars at the toy store. How many toy cars are there?

_____ toy cars

110

Lesson 55

© Houghton Mifflin Harcourt Publishing Company

Addition: Regroup Ones and Tens

OBJECTIVE Record 3-digit addition using the standard algorithm with possible regrouping of both ones and tens.

CC.2.NBT.7

Sometimes, you may need to regroup
more than once.

189
+623

Step 1 Add the ones.
There are 12 ones in all.
Regroup 12 ones as 1 ten 2 ones.

	1	8	9
+	6	2	3
			2

Step 2 Add the tens.
There are 11 tens in all.
Regroup 11 tens as 1 hundred 1 ten.

	1	8	9
+	6	2	3
		1	2

Step 3 Add the hundreds.
There are 8 hundreds in all.

	1	8	9
+	6	2	3
8		1	2

Write the sum.

1.

	2	7	8
+	4	6	5

2.

	1	5	7
+	7	7	1

3.

	3	6	4
+	4	1	9

CC.2.NBT.7

Addition: Regroup Ones and Tens

Write the sum.

1.
```
  5 4 7
+ 4 3 5
```

2.
```
  3 6 7
+ 2 8 4
```

3.
```
  4 8 5
+ 4 5 6
```

4.
```
  1 8 7
+ 3 0 6
```

5.
```
  6 4 7
+ 1 2 8
```

6.
```
  5 2 3
+ 1 7 4
```

7.
```
  2 5 5
+ 2 3 1
```

8.
```
  2 9 4
+ 1 7 6
```

9.
```
  3 7 5
+ 3 6 4
```

Problem Solving

Solve. Write or draw to explain.

10. Saul and Luisa each scored 167 points on a computer game. How many points did they score?

_____ points

Problem Solving · 3-Digit Subtraction

OBJECTIVE Solve problems involving 3-digit subtraction by using the strategy *make a model*.

CC.2.NBT.7

There were 237 books on the shelves.

Mr. Davies took 126 books off the shelves.

How many books were still on the shelves?

Unlock the Problem

What do I need to find?

how many books

were still on the shelves.

What information do I need to use?

There were 237 books on the shelves.

Mr. Davies took 126 books off the shelves.

Show how to solve the problem.

There were _____ books still on the shelves.

Make a model to solve. Then draw a quick picture of your model.

1. Mr. Cho has 256 pencils.
   Then he sells 132 pencils.
   How many pencils does
   he have now?

_____ pencils

© Houghton Mifflin Harcourt Publishing Company

CC.2.NBT.7

Problem Solving • 3-Digit Subtraction

**Make a model to solve. Then draw
a quick picture of your model.**

I. On Saturday, 770 people went to the snack
shop. On Sunday, 628 people went. How
many more people went to the snack shop
on Saturday than on Sunday?

_____ more people

2. There were 395 lemon ice cups at the snack
shop. People bought 177 lemon ice cups.
How many lemon ice cups are still at the
snack shop?

_____ cups

3. There were 576 bottles of water at the
snack shop. People bought 469 bottles of
water. How many bottles of water are at the
snack shop now?

_____ bottles

4. There were 279 bags of apple chips at the
snack shop. Then 134 bags of apple chips
were bought. How many bags of apple chips
are at the snack shop now?

_____ bags

3-Digit Subtraction: Regroup Tens

LESSON 58

OBJECTIVE Record 3-digit subtraction using the standard algorithm with possible regrouping of tens.

Subtract.   463
         − 317

Are there enough ones to subtract 7? **no**

Regroup 1 ten as 10 ones.

Hundreds	Tens	Ones
4	6	3
− 3	1	7

There are **13** ones

and **5** tens.

Subtract the ones.

$13 - 7 =$ **6**

Hundreds	Tens	Ones
	5	13
4	6̶	3̶
− 3	1	7
		6

Subtract the tens.

$5 - 1 =$ **4**

Subtract the hundreds.

$4 - 3 =$ **1**

Hundreds	Tens	Ones
	5	13
4	6̶	3̶
− 3	1	7
1	4	6

So, $463 - 317 = 146$.

Solve. Write the difference.

1.

Hundreds	Tens	Ones
8	6	2
− 3	2	8

2.

Hundreds	Tens	Ones
6	7	8
− 2	4	5

CC.2.NBT.7

3-Digit Subtraction: Regroup Tens

Solve. Write the difference.

1.

Hundreds	Tens	Ones
	☐	☐
7	7	4
− 2	3	6

2.

Hundreds	Tens	Ones
	☐	☐
5	5	1
− 1	1	3

3.

Hundreds	Tens	Ones
	☐	☐
4	8	9
− 2	7	3

4.

Hundreds	Tens	Ones
	☐	☐
7	7	2
− 2	5	4

Problem Solving

Solve. Write or draw to explain.

5. There were 985 pencils. Some pencils were sold. Then there were 559 pencils left. How many pencils were sold?

_____ pencils

LESSON 59

3-Digit Subtraction: Regroup Hundreds

CC.2.NBT.7

OBJECTIVE Record 3-digit subtraction using the standard algorithm with possible regrouping of hundreds.

Subtract. $\begin{array}{r} 326 \\ -174 \\ \hline \end{array}$

Subtract the ones.

$6 - 4 = \underline{2}$

Are there enough tens to subtract 7 tens? __no__

Regroup 1 hundred as 10 tens.

Hundreds	Tens	Ones
2	12	
3	2	6
− 1	7	4
		2

Now there are __12__ tens

and __2__ hundreds.

Subtract the tens.

$12 - 7 = \underline{5}$

Subtract the hundreds.

$2 - 1 = \underline{1}$

So, $326 - 174 = 152$.

Hundreds	Tens	Ones
2	12	
3	2	6
− 1	7	4
1	5	2

Solve. Write the difference.

1.

Hundreds	Tens	Ones
6	7	9
− 2	6	1

2.

Hundreds	Tens	Ones
5	2	5
− 2	9	3

3-Digit Subtraction: Regroup Hundreds

Solve. Write the difference.

1.

Hundreds	Tens	Ones
☐	☐	☐
7	2	7
− 2	5	6

2.

Hundreds	Tens	Ones
☐	☐	☐
9	6	7
− 1	5	3

3.

☐	☐	☐
6	3	9
− 4	7	2

4.

☐	☐	☐
4	4	8
− 3	6	3

Problem Solving

Solve. Write or draw to explain.

5. There were 537 people in the parade. 254 of these people were playing an instrument. How many people were not playing an instrument?

_____ people

LESSON 60

Subtraction: Regroup Hundreds and Tens

CC.2.NBT.7

OBJECTIVE Record 3-digit subtraction using the standard algorithm with possible regrouping of both hundreds and tens.

You may need to regroup more than once.

```
  282
- 198
```

Regroup 1 ten as 10 ones. Subtract the ones.	Regroup 1 hundred as 10 tens. Subtract the tens.	Subtract the hundreds.
$\begin{array}{r} 7\,12 \\ 2\,\cancel{8}\,\cancel{2} \\ -1\,9\,8 \\ \hline 4 \end{array}$	$\begin{array}{r} 17 \\ 1\,\cancel{7}\,12 \\ 2\,\cancel{8}\,\cancel{2} \\ -1\,9\,8 \\ \hline 84 \end{array}$	$\begin{array}{r} 17 \\ 1\,\cancel{7}\,12 \\ \cancel{2}\,\cancel{8}\,\cancel{2} \\ -1\,9\,8 \\ \hline 84 \end{array}$

Solve. Write the difference.

1.
```
  481
- 176
```

2.
```
  746
-  28
```

3.
```
  331
- 148
```

4.
```
  395
- 131
```

5.
```
  524
- 265
```

6.
```
  748
- 603
```

CC.2.NBT.7

Subtraction: Regroup Hundreds and Tens

Solve. Write the difference.

1.
```
  8 1 6
- 3 4 5
```

2.
```
  9 4 2
- 1 6 3
```

3.
```
  7 9 6
- 4 6 8
```

4.
```
  7 2 3
- 5 4 3
```

5.
```
  9 8 6
- 7 1 2
```

6.
```
  5 4 7
- 2 8 9
```

Problem Solving

Solve.

7. Anne's coloring book has 432 pages.
She has already colored 178 pages.
How many pages in the book are
left to color?

_____ pages

LESSON 61

Regrouping with Zeros

OBJECTIVE Record subtraction using the standard algorithm when there are zeros in the minuend.

CC.2.NBT.7

Subtract 138 from 305.

There are not enough ones to subtract 8.

Since there are 0 tens, regroup 3 hundreds as 2 hundreds 10 tens.

Hundreds	Tens	Ones

$$\begin{array}{r} 2\ 10 \\ \cancel{3}\ \cancel{0}\ 5 \\ -1\ 3\ 8 \\ \hline \end{array}$$

Then regroup 10 tens 5 ones as 9 tens 15 ones.

Subtract the ones.

$15 - 8 = 7$

Hundreds	Tens	Ones

$$\begin{array}{r} 9 \\ 2\ 10\ 15 \\ \cancel{3}\ \cancel{0}\ \cancel{5} \\ -1\ 3\ 8 \\ \hline 7 \end{array}$$

Subtract the tens.

$9 - 3 = 6$

Subtract the hundreds.

$2 - 1 = 1$

So, $305 - 138 = \underline{167}$.

Hundreds	Tens	Ones

$$\begin{array}{r} 9 \\ 2\ 10\ 15 \\ \cancel{3}\ \cancel{0}\ \cancel{5} \\ -1\ 3\ 8 \\ \hline 1\ 6\ 7 \end{array}$$

Solve. Write the difference.

1.

$$\begin{array}{r} 8\ 0\ 1 \\ -3\ 7\ 5 \\ \hline \end{array}$$

2.

$$\begin{array}{r} 6\ 9\ 3 \\ -2\ 4\ 1 \\ \hline \end{array}$$

3.

$$\begin{array}{r} 9\ 0\ 7 \\ -6\ 2\ 4 \\ \hline \end{array}$$

CC.2.NBT.7

Regrouping with Zeros

Solve. Write the difference.

1.

$$\begin{array}{r} 806 \\ -345 \\ \hline \end{array}$$

2.

$$\begin{array}{r} 902 \\ -783 \\ \hline \end{array}$$

3.

$$\begin{array}{r} 794 \\ -268 \\ \hline \end{array}$$

4.

$$\begin{array}{r} 687 \\ -144 \\ \hline \end{array}$$

5.

$$\begin{array}{r} 505 \\ -167 \\ \hline \end{array}$$

6.

$$\begin{array}{r} 307 \\ -154 \\ \hline \end{array}$$

Problem Solving

Solve.

7. There are 303 students.
There are 147 girls.
How many boys are there?

_____ boys

© Houghton Mifflin Harcourt Publishing Company

Count On and Count Back by 10 and 100

OBJECTIVE Identify 10 more, 10 less, 100 more, or 100 less than a given number.

CC.2.NBT.8

10 less than 234

2 hundreds 2 tens 4 ones.

2̲2̲4̲

Notice what digit changes.

100 less than 234

1 hundred 3 tens 4 ones.

1̲3̲4̲

10 more than 234

2 hundreds 4 tens 4 ones.

2̲4̲4̲

100 more than 234

3 hundreds 3 tens 4 ones.

3̲3̲4̲

Write the number.

1. 10 more than 719

_____

2. 10 less than 246

_____

3. 100 more than 291

_____

4. 100 less than 687

_____

5. 10 less than 568

_____

6. 100 more than 649

_____

CC.2.NBT.8

Count On and Count Back by 10 and 100

Write the number.

1. 10 more than 451

_____

2. 10 less than 770

_____

3. 100 more than 367

_____

4. 100 less than 895

_____

5. 10 less than 812

_____

6. 100 more than 543

_____

7. 10 more than 218

_____

8. 100 more than 379

_____

9. 100 less than 324

_____

10. 10 less than 829

_____

Problem Solving

Solve. Write or draw to explain.

11. Sarah has 128 stickers. Alex has 10 fewer
stickers than Sarah. How many stickers
does Alex have?

_____ stickers

CC.2.NBT.8

LESSON 63

Algebra • Number Patterns

OBJECTIVE Extend number patterns by counting on by tens or hundreds.

Find a counting pattern.

421, 431, 441, 451, ▩, ▩

Which digit changes from number to number?

The ___tens___ digit changes.

How does it change?

by ___one___ each time

Look at the chart. Find the next two numbers in the pattern.

401	402	403	404	405	406	407	408	409	410
411	412	413	414	415	416	417	418	419	420
421	422	423	424	425	426	427	428	429	430
431	432	433	434	435	436	437	438	439	440
441	442	443	444	445	446	447	448	449	450
451	452	453	454	455	456	457	458	459	460
461	462	463	464	465	466	467	468	469	470
471	472	473	474	475	476	477	478	479	480
481	482	483	484	485	486	487	488	489	490
491	492	493	494	495	496	497	498	499	500

The next two numbers are ___461___ and ___471___.

Look at the digits to find the next two numbers.

1. 937, 947, 957, 967, ▩, ▩

   The next two numbers are _____ and _____.

2. 135, 235, 335, 435, ▩, ▩

   The next two numbers are _____ and _____.

Algebra • Number Patterns

Look at the digits to find the next two numbers.

1. 232, 242, 252, 262,

The next two numbers are _____ and _____ .

2. 185, 285, 385, 485, ▪, ▪

The next two numbers are _____ and _____ .

3. 428, 528, 628, 728, ▪, ▪

The next two numbers are _____ and _____ .

4. 654, 664, 674, 684, ▪, ▪

The next two numbers are _____ and _____ .

5. 333, 433, 533, 633, ▪, ▪

The next two numbers are _____ and _____ .

Problem Solving

6. What are the missing numbers in the pattern?

431, 441, 451, 461, , 481, 491,

The missing numbers are _____ and _____ .

Model Regrouping for Addition

LESSON 64

OBJECTIVE Model 2-digit addition with regrouping.

CC.2.NBT.9

Add 18 and 25.

Show 18 and 25 with ▭▭▭▭▭ ▫.

Count the ones.

How many ones are there? __13__ ones

Can you make a ten? __yes__

Tens	Ones

Trade 10 ones for 1 ten.

This is called regrouping.

Tens	Ones

Count the tens. How many tens are there? __4__ tens

Count the ones. How many ones are there? __3__ ones

__4__ tens __3__ ones is the same as __43__ .

Tens	Ones

Write how many tens and ones in the sum. Write the sum.

1. Add 46 and 19.

Tens	Ones

_____ tens _____ ones

_____

2. Add 45 and 27.

Tens	Ones

_____ tens _____ ones

_____

3. Add 58 and 38.

Tens	Ones

_____ tens _____ ones

_____

Model Regrouping for Addition

Draw to show the regrouping. Write how many
tens and ones in the sum. Write the sum.

1. Add 63 and 9.

Tens	Ones

_____ tens _____ ones

_____

2. Add 25 and 58.

Tens	Ones

_____ tens _____ ones

_____

3. Add 58 and 18.

Tens	Ones

_____ tens _____ ones

_____

4. Add 64 and 26.

Tens	Ones

_____ tens _____ ones

_____

5. Add 17 and 77.

Tens	Ones

_____ tens _____ ones

_____

6. Add 16 and 39.

Tens	Ones

_____ tens _____ ones

_____

Problem Solving

Choose a way to solve.
Write or draw to explain.

7. Cathy has 43 leaves in her collection.
Jane has 38 leaves. How many leaves
do the two children have?   _____ leaves

Name _____

 LESSON 65

Model Regrouping for Subtraction

OBJECTIVE Model 2-digit subtraction with regrouping.

CC.2.NBT.9

Subtract 37 from 65.

Are there enough ones to subtract 7? __no__
So, you will need to regroup.

Trade 1 ten for 10 ones.

Tens	Ones

Subtract the ones. Then subtract the tens.

15 ones − 7 ones = ___8___ ones

5 tens − 3 tens = ___2___ tens

___2___ tens ___8___ ones is the same as ___28___.

The difference is ___28___.

Draw to show the regrouping. Write the tens and ones that are in the difference. Write the number.

1. Subtract 18 from 43.

Tens	Ones

_____ tens _____ ones

_____

2. Subtract 19 from 55.

Tens	Ones

_____ tens _____ ones

_____

Model Regrouping for Subtraction

Draw to show the regrouping. Write the difference two ways.
Write the tens and ones. Write the number.

1. Subtract 9 from 35.

Tens	Ones

____ tens ____ ones

____

2. Subtract 14 from 52.

Tens	Ones

____ tens ____ ones

____

3. Subtract 17 from 46.

Tens	Ones

____ tens ____ ones

____

4. Subtract 28 from 63.

Tens	Ones

____ tens ____ ones

____

Problem Solving

Choose a way to solve. Write or draw to explain.

5. Mr. Ortega made 51 cookies. He gave
14 cookies away. How many cookies
does he have now?

____ cookies

Measure With Inch Models

OBJECTIVE Use concrete models to measure the lengths of objects in inches.

CC.2.MD.1

Place tiles on the squares. How many tiles? __3__ tiles
Each tile is about 1 inch long.

How long is the ribbon? about __3__ inches

Use color tiles. Measure the length of the object in inches.

1.

about _____ inches

2.

about _____ inches

3.

about _____ inches

CC.2.MD.1

Measure with Inch Models

**Use color tiles. Measure the length
of the object in inches.**

1.

about _____ inches

2.

about _____ inches

3.

about _____ inches

4.

about _____ inches

Problem Solving

5. Look around your classroom.
Find an object that is about 4 inches long.
Draw and label the object.

© Houghton Mifflin Harcourt Publishing Company

LESSON 67

Make and Use a Ruler

OBJECTIVE Make an inch ruler and use it to measure the lengths of objects.

CC.2.MD.1

Use a paper strip. Mark the sides of a color tile.
Mark 6 tiles. Color each part.

Each part is about ___**1 inch**___ long.

Line up the left edge of the bracelet with
the first mark. Count the inches.

The bracelet is about ___5___ inches long.

Measure the length with your ruler.
Count the inches.

1.

about _____ inches

2.

about _____ inches

CC.2.MD.1

Make and Use a Ruler

Measure the length with your ruler. Count the inches.

1.

about _____ inches

2.

about _____ inches

3.

about _____ inches

4.

about _____ inches

Problem Solving

5. Use your ruler. Measure the width
of this page in inches.

about _____ inches

LESSON 68

Measure with an Inch Ruler

OBJECTIVE Measure the lengths of objects to the nearest inch using an inch ruler.

CC.2.MD.1

---

1. Line up one end with 0.

2. Find the inch mark closest to the other end.

3. Read the number of inches at that mark.

The ribbon is about ___3___ inches long.

Measure the length to the nearest inch.

1.

_____

_____ inches

2.

_____ inches

3.

_____ inches

CC.2.MD.1

Measure with an Inch Ruler

Measure the length to the nearest inch.

1.

_____ inches

2.

_____ inches

3.

_____ inches

4. ⬡⬡⬡⬡⬡⬡⬡⬡⬡⬡⬡⬡⬡⬡⬡⬡⬡⬡⬡⬡⬡

_____ inches

Problem Solving

5. Measure the string. What is its total length?

_____ inches

LESSON 69

Choose a Tool

OBJECTIVE Select appropriate tools for measuring different lengths.

Use an inch ruler to measure short lengths.

Use a yardstick to measure greater lengths.

Use a measuring tape to measure lengths
that are not flat.

**Choose the best tool for measuring the real object.
Then measure and record the length.**

I. a pencil

Tool: _____

Length: _____

---

2. a chalkboard

Tool: _____

Length: _____

Choose a Tool

Choose the best tool for measuring the real object. Then measure and record the length or distance.

inch ruler
yardstick
measuring tape

1. the length of your desk

Tool: _____

Length: _____

2. the distance around a basket

Tool: _____

Length: _____

Problem Solving

> Choose the better tool for measuring.
> Explain your choice.
>
> **3.** Mark wants to measure the length of his room. Should he use an inch ruler or a yardstick?
>
> Mark should use _____ because
>
> _____
>
> _____

LESSON 70

Measure with a Centimeter Model

OBJECTIVE Use a concrete model to measure the lengths of objects in centimeters.

```
1   2   3   4   5   6   7   8
```

Place unit cubes on the squares.

How many cubes long is the pencil?

The pencil is __8__ cubes long.

Each unit cube is about 1 centimeter long.

So, the pencil is about __8__ centimeters long.

Use a unit cube. Measure the length in centimeters.

1.

about _____ centimeters

2.

about _____ centimeters

3.

about _____ centimeters

CC.2.MD.1

Measure with a Centimeter Model

Use a unit cube. Measure the length in centimeters.

1.

about _____ centimeters

2.

about _____ centimeters

3.

about _____ centimeters

4.

about _____ centimeters

Problem Solving

Solve. Write or draw to explain.

5. Susan has a pencil that is 3 centimeters shorter than this string. How long is the pencil?

about _____ centimeters

Measure with a Centimeter Ruler

LESSON 71

OBJECTIVE Measure lengths of objects to the nearest centimeter using a centimeter ruler.

CC.2.MD.1

Line up the left end of the ribbon with the zero mark on the ruler.

Which centimeter mark is closest to the other end of the ribbon?

The ribbon is about __7__ centimeters long.

Measure the length to the nearest centimeter.

1.

_____ centimeters

2.

_____ centimeters

3.

_____ centimeters

CC.2.MD.1

Measure with a Centimeter Ruler

Measure the length to the nearest centimeter.

1.

_____ centimeters

2.

_____ centimeters

3.

_____ centimeters

Problem Solving

4. Draw a string that is about 8 centimeters long.
Then use a centimeter ruler to check the length.

Measure in Inches and Feet

LESSON 72

OBJECTIVE Measure the lengths of objects in both inches and feet to explore the inverse relationship between size and number of units.

CC.2.MD.2

The real folder is about 12 inches wide.

The real folder is also about 1 foot wide.

12 inches is the same as 1 foot.

Measure to the nearest inch.
Then measure to the nearest foot.

	Find the real object.	Measure.
1.	desk	_____ inches _____ feet
2.	rug	_____ inches _____ feet
3.	map	_____ inches _____ feet

Measure in Inches and Feet

Measure to the nearest inch.
Then measure to the nearest foot.

Find the real object.	Measure.
1. bookcase	_____ inches _____ feet
2. window	_____ inches _____ feet
3. chair	_____ inches _____ feet

Problem Solving

4. Jake has a piece of yarn that is 4 feet long.
   Blair has a piece of yarn that is 4 inches long.
   Who has the longer piece of yarn? Explain.

   _____

   _____

LESSON 73 Centimeters and Meters

OBJECTIVE Measure the lengths of objects in both centimeters and meters to explore the inverse relationship between size and number of units.

CC.2.MD.2

You can measure longer
lengths in meters.

1 meter is the same as
100 centimeters.

The real board is about 100 centimeters tall.
So, the real board is about 1 meter tall.

Measure to the nearest centimeter.
Then measure to the nearest meter.

Find the real object.	Measure.
1. **desk**	_____ centimeters _____ meters
2. **door**	_____ centimeters _____ meters
3. **classroom floor**	_____ centimeters _____ meters

Centimeters and Meters

Measure to the nearest centimeter.
Then measure to the nearest meter.

Find the real object.	Measure.
1. bookcase	_____ centimeters _____ meters
2. window	_____ centimeters _____ meters
3. map	_____ centimeters _____ meters

Problem Solving

4. Sally will measure the length of a wall in both centimeters and meters. Will there be fewer centimeters or fewer meters? Explain.

_____

_____

LESSON 74 **Estimate Lengths in Inches**

OBJECTIVE Estimate the lengths of objects by mentally partitioning the lengths into inches.

CC.2.MD.3

The bead is 1 inch long. How many beads will fit on the string?
Four beads will fit on the string.

About how long is the string? The string is about ___4___ inches long.

Circle the best estimate for the length of the string.

1.

2 inches   4 inches   6 inches

2.

1 inch   3 inches   5 inches

3.

1 inch   2 inches   4 inches

4.

5 inches   8 inches   10 inches

Estimate Lengths in Inches

The bead is 1 inch long. Circle the best estimate for the length of the string.

1.

1 inch   4 inches   7 inches

2.

3 inches   6 inches   9 inches

3.

2 inches   3 inches   6 inches

4.

2 inches   5 inches   8 inches

Problem Solving

Solve. Write or draw to explain.

5. Ashley has some beads. Each bead is 2 inches long. How many beads will fit on a string that is 8 inches long?

_____ beads

Estimate Lengths in Feet
OBJECTIVE Estimate the lengths of objects in feet.

CC.2.MD.3

About how many rulers will fit along the length
of a real whiteboard?

A 12-inch ruler is
1 foot long.

$\underset{3}{\_\_\_}$ rulers, or $\underset{3}{\_\_\_}$ feet

---

**Find each object. Estimate how many 12-inch rulers will
be about the same length as the object.**

1. chalkboard

Estimate: _____ rulers, or _____ feet

---

2. poster

Estimate: _____ rulers, or _____ feet

CC.2.MD.3

Estimate Lengths in Feet

Find each object.
Estimate how many 12-inch rulers will
be about the same length as the object.

1. door

Estimate: _____ rulers, or _____ feet

---

2. flag

Estimate: _____ rulers, or _____ feet

---

3. wall of a small room

Estimate: _____ rulers, or _____ feet

Problem Solving

Solve. Write or draw to explain.

4. Mr. and Mrs. Baker place 12-inch rulers along the
length of a rug. They each line up 3 rulers along the
edge of the rug. What is the length of the rug?

about _____ feet

LESSON 76

Estimate Lengths in Centimeters

OBJECTIVE Estimate lengths of objects in centimeters by comparing them to known lengths.

CC.2.MD.3

The ribbon is about 8 centimeters long. How can you find the most reasonable estimate for the length of the string?

ribbon

string

I centimeter

(6 centimeters)

10 centimeters

Think: 1 centimeter is not reasonable because the string is much longer than 1 cube.

Think: 10 centimeters is not reasonable because the string is shorter than the ribbon.

---

1. The rope is about 7 centimeters long. Circle the best estimate for the length of the yarn.

rope

yarn

5 centimeters   9 centimeters   14 centimeters

---

2. The pencil is about 10 centimeters long. Circle the best estimate for the length of the ribbon.

pencil   ribbon

5 centimeters   9 centimeters   12 centimeters

CC.2.MD.3

Estimate Lengths in Centimeters

1. The toothpick is about 6 centimeters long. Circle the best estimate for the length of the yarn.

6 centimeters

9 centimeters

12 centimeters

2. The pen is about 11 centimeters long. Circle the best estimate for the length of the eraser.

4 centimeters

10 centimeters

14 centimeters

3. The string is about 6 centimeters long. Circle the best estimate for the length of the crayon.

5 centimeters

9 centimeters

14 centimeters

Problem Solving

4. The string is about 6 centimeters long. Draw a pencil that is about 12 centimeters long.

LESSON 77 **Estimate Lengths in Meters**

OBJECTIVE Estimate the lengths of objects in meters.

Estimate the length of the chalk tray.

The chalk tray is about the same
length as 2 meter sticks.

So, the chalk tray is about _____2_____ meters long.

Find the real object.
Estimate its length in meters.

1. window

about _____ meters

---

2. bookshelf

about _____ meters

Estimate Lengths in Meters

Find the real object.
Estimate its length in meters.

1. poster

about _____ meters

2. chalkboard

about _____ meters

3. bookshelf

about _____ meters

Problem Solving

4. Barbara and Luke each placed 2 meter sticks end-to-end along the length of a large table. About how long is the table?

about _____ meters

LESSON 78

Measure and Compare Lengths

OBJECTIVE Measure and then find the difference in the lengths of two objects.

 CC.2.MD.4

Which object is longer? How much longer?

1. Measure the leaf.

The leaf is ___9___ centimeters.

2. Measure the stick.

The stick is ___5___ centimeters.

3. Complete the number sentence to find the difference.

___9___ − ___5___ = ___4___
centimeters centimeters centimeters

The leaf is ___4___ centimeters longer than the stick.

Measure the length of each object. Write a number sentence to find the difference between the lengths.

1.

_____ centimeters

_____ centimeters

_____ − _____ = _____
centimeters centimeters centimeters

The string is _____ centimeters longer than the paper clip.

Measure and Compare Lengths

Measure the length of each object. Write a number sentence to find the difference between the lengths.

1.

_____ centimeters

_____ centimeters

_____ – _____ = _____
centimeters centimeters centimeters

The craft stick is _____ centimeters longer than the chalk.

2.

_____ centimeters

_____ centimeters

_____ – _____ = _____
centimeters centimeters centimeters

The string is _____ centimeters longer than the toothpick.

Problem Solving

Solve. Write or draw to explain.

3. A string is 11 centimeters long, a ribbon is 24 centimeters long, and a large paper clip is 5 centimeters long. How much longer is the ribbon than the string?

_____ centimeters

LESSON 79

Problem Solving • Add and Subtract in Inches

CC.2.MD.5

OBJECTIVE Solve addition and subtraction problems involving the lengths of objects by using the strategy *draw a diagram*.

Zack has two strings. One string is 12 inches long and the other string is 5 inches long. How long are Zack's strings altogether?

Unlock the Problem

What do I need to find?

how long Zack's

strings are

What information do I need to use?

One string is ___12___ inches long.

The other string is ___5___ inches long.

Show how to solve the problem.

$$12 + 5 = \blacksquare$$

The strings are ___17___ inches long in all.

Write a number sentence using a ■ for the missing number. Solve.

1. Sara has two pieces of yarn. Each piece is 7 inches long. How many inches of yarn does she have?

_____   Sara has _____ inches of yarn.

CC.2.MD.5

Problem Solving • Add and Subtract in Inches

Draw a diagram. Write a number sentence using a ▮ for the missing number. Solve.

1. Molly had a ribbon that was 23 inches long.
   She cut 7 inches off the ribbon. How long is
   her ribbon now?

0 1 2 3 4 5 6 7 8 9 10 11 12 13 14 15 16 17 18 19 20 21 22 23 24 25

_____

Molly's ribbon is _____ inches long now.

2. Jed has a paper clip chain that is 11 inches long.
   He adds 7 inches of paper clips to the chain.
   How long is the paper clip chain now?

0 1 2 3 4 5 6 7 8 9 10 11 12 13 14 15 16 17 18 19 20 21 22 23 24 25

_____

The paper clip chain is _____ inches long now.

LESSON 80

Problem Solving · Add and Subtract Lengths

CC.2.MD.6

OBJECTIVE Solve problems involving adding and subtracting lengths by using the strategy *draw a diagram.*

Christy has a ribbon that is 12 meters long. Erin has a ribbon that is 9 meters long. How many meters of ribbon do they have?

Unlock the Problem

What do I need to find?	**What information do I need to use?**
how much ribbon they have	Christy has __12__ meters of ribbon. Erin has __9__ meters of ribbon.

Show how to solve the problem.

```
          12                          9
|--------------------------|--------------------------|
```

← 0 1 2 3 4 5 6 7 8 9 10 11 12 13 14 15 16 17 18 19 20 21 22 23 24 25 →

$12 + 9 = \blacksquare$

21

They have __21__ meters of ribbon.

Write a number sentence using a ■ for the missing number. Then solve.

1. Lucas has one string that is 9 meters long and another string that is 8 meters long. How many meters of string are there?

← 0 1 2 3 4 5 6 7 8 9 10 11 12 13 14 15 16 17 18 19 20 21 22 23 24 25 →

_____   _____ meters of string in all

CC.2.MD.6

Problem Solving • Add and Subtract Lengths

**Draw a diagram. Write a number sentence using
a ▮ for the missing number. Then solve.**

1. A straw is 20 centimeters long. Mr. Jones
cuts off 8 centimeters of the straw. How long
is the straw now?

_____

The straw is _____ centimeters long now.

2. Ella has a piece of blue yarn that is 14 centimeters long.
She has a piece of red yarn that is 9 centimeters long.
How many centimeters of yarn does she have altogether?

_____

She has _____ centimeters of yarn altogether.

LESSON 81

Time to the Hour and Half Hour

OBJECTIVE Tell and write time to the hour and half hour.

CC.2.MD.7

It is zero minutes after the hour.
Look at how you write this time.

It is 30 minutes after the hour.
Look at how you write this time.

Look at the clock hands. Write the time.

1.

2.

3.

4.

5.

6.

CC.2.MD.7

Time to the Hour and Half Hour

Look at the clock hands. Write the time.

1.

2.

3.

4.

5.

6.

Problem Solving

7. Amy's music lesson begins at 4:00.
Draw hands on the clock to show
this time.

© Houghton Mifflin Harcourt Publishing Company

Name _____

LESSON 82

Time to 5 Minutes

OBJECTIVE Tell and write time to the nearest five minutes.

CC.2.MD.7

The minute hand moves from one number to the next in 5 minutes.

Start at the 12. Count by fives.

Stop at the number the minute hand points to.

The hour is 8 o'clock.

It is 20 minutes after 8:00.

Look at the clock hands. Write the time.

1.

2.

3.

4.

5.

6.

© Houghton Mifflin Harcourt Publishing Company

Measurement and Data

163

CC.2.MD.7

Time to 5 Minutes

Look at the clock hands. Write the time.

1.

2.

3.

4.

5.

6.

Problem Solving

Draw the minute hand to show the time. Then write the time.

7. My hour hand points between the 4 and the 5. My minute hand points to the 9. What time do I show?

Name _____

Practice Telling Time

OBJECTIVE Practice telling time to the nearest five minutes.

Use the clock hands to tell time.
First find the hour.

The hour is ___11___.

Now figure out minutes.
When the minute hand points
to the 3 it is quarter past.

It is ___15___ minutes past 11.

The time is ___quarter past 11___.

Draw the minute hand to show the time.
Write the time.

1. quarter past 9	**2.** 30 minutes after 11

3. half past 10	**4.** 15 minutes after 6

Practice Telling Time

Draw the minute hand to show the time. Write the time.

1. quarter past 7

2. half past 3

3. 50 minutes after 1

4. quarter past 11

5. 15 minutes after 8

6. 5 minutes after 6

Problem Solving

Draw hands on the clock to solve.

7. Josh got to school at half past 8.
Show this time on the clock.

LESSON 84

A.M. and P.M.

OBJECTIVE Tell and write time using a.m. and p.m.

CC.2.MD.7

A.M. times *start* after midnight.
A.M. times *end* before noon.
get dressed for school

  A.M.

 7:30

P.M. times *start* after noon.
P.M. times *end* before midnight.
tell a bedtime story

P.M.

7:30

Write the time. Then circle A.M. or P.M.

1. finish homework

A.M.

P.M.

2. go to morning recess

A.M.

P.M.

3. eat breakfast

A.M.

P.M.

4. get ready for bed

A.M.

P.M.

Measurement and Data

167

A.M. and P.M.

Write the time. Then circle A.M. or P.M.

1. walk the dog

A.M.

P.M.

2. finish breakfast

A.M.

P.M.

3. put on pajamas

A.M.

P.M.

4. read a bedtime story

A.M.

P.M.

Problem Solving

Use the list of times. Complete the story.

5. Jess woke up at _____. She got on

the bus at _____ and went to school.

She left school at _____.

| 3:15 P.M. |
| 8:30 A.M. |
| 7:00 A.M. |

LESSON 85

Dimes, Nickels, and Pennies

OBJECTIVE Find the total values of collections of dimes, nickels, and pennies.

CC.2.MD.8

I dime
10¢

Count dimes by tens.

10¢, 20¢, 30¢

I nickel
5¢

Count nickels by fives.

5¢, 10¢, 15¢

I penny
1¢

Count pennies by ones.

1¢, 2¢, 3¢

Count on by tens.

Count on by fives.

Count on by ones.

10¢, 20¢, 25¢, 30¢, 31¢

31¢

total value

Count on to find the total value.

1.

total value

_____

2.

total value

_____

Dimes, Nickels, and Pennies

Count on to find the total value.

1. ☐

_____ total value

2.   ☐

_____ total value

3. ☐

_____ total value

4. ☐

_____ total value

Problem Solving

Solve. Write or draw to explain.

5. Aaron has 5 dimes and 2 nickels.
How much money does Aaron have?

_____

LESSON 86

Quarters

OBJECTIVE Find the total values of collections of quarters, dimes, nickels, and pennies.

CC.2.MD.8

I quarter
25¢

Count by twenty-fives.

25¢, 50¢, 75¢ _____

Count by twenty-fives. Count by tens. Count by ones.

25¢, 50¢, 60¢, 61¢ _____

 61¢
total value

Count on to find the total value.

1.

_____

[ ] total value

2.

_____

[ ] total value

Quarters

Count on to find the total value.

1.

_____ total value

2.

_____ total value

3.

_____ total value

Problem Solving

Read the clue. Choose the name of a coin from the box to answer the question.

nickel	dime
quarter	penny

4. I have the same value as a group
of 2 dimes and 1 nickel.
What coin am I?

_____

LESSON 87

Count Collections

OBJECTIVE Order coins in a collection by value and then find the total value.

CC.2.MD.8

Draw the coins in order by value. Start
with the coin that has the greatest value.

(25¢) (10¢) (5¢) (1¢)

Start at 25¢. Count on.

25¢, 35¢, 40¢, 41¢ _____ total value **41¢**

Draw the coins in order. Find the total value.

1.

total value _____

2.

total value _____

3.

total value _____

Name _____

CC.2.MD.8

Count Collections

Draw and label the coins from greatest
to least value. Find the total value.

1.

_____

2.

_____

3.

_____

Problem Solving

Solve. Write or draw to explain.

4. Rebecca has these coins. She
spends 1 quarter. How much
money does she have left?

_____

LESSON 88

Show Amounts in Two Ways

OBJECTIVE Represent money amounts less than a dollar using two different combinations of coins.

CC.2.MD.8

You can show the same amount in different ways.

Trade 2 nickels for 1 dime.

15¢

Count the coins.

5, 10, 15

15¢

Count the coins.

10, 15

Use coins. Show the amount in two ways.
Draw and label the coins.

1.

45¢

25¢   10¢   10¢

2.

32¢

Show Amounts in Two Ways

Use coins. Show the amounts in two ways.
Draw and label the coins.

1.

39¢

2.

70¢

3.

57¢

Problem Solving

4. Madeline uses fewer than 5 coins
to pay 60¢. Draw coins to show
two ways she could pay 60¢.

LESSON 89

One Dollar

OBJECTIVE Show one dollar in a variety of ways.

CC.2.MD.8

One dollar has the same value as 100 cents.

You can write
one dollar like this:
$1.00

Count on to 100¢ to show $1.00.

$1.00
total value

25¢, 50¢, 75¢, 100¢

Draw more coins to show $1.00. Write the total value.

1. dimes

_____

---

2. nickels

_____

One Dollar

Circle coins to make $1.00.
Cross out the coins you do not use.

1.

2.

3.

Problem Solving

4. Draw more coins to show $1.00.

LESSON 90

Amounts Greater Than $1

OBJECTIVE Find and record the total value for money amounts greater than $1.

CC.2.MD.8

---

1. Count on and circle the coins that make one dollar.

2. Count on from 100¢ to find the total value for the whole group of coins.

110¢   120¢

3. 120¢ is the same as 1 dollar and 20 cents.

Write _____$1.20_____.

Circle the money that makes $1. Then write the total value of the money shown.

1.

_____

2.

_____

CC.2.MD.8

Amounts Greater Than $1

Circle the money that makes $1.00. Then write the total value of the money shown.

1.

_____

2.

_____

3.

_____

Problem Solving

Solve. Write or draw to explain.

4. Grace found 3 quarters, 3 dimes, and 1 nickel in her pocket. How much money did she find?

_____

Lesson 90

LESSON 91

Problem Solving • Money

OBJECTIVE Solve word problems involving money by using the strategy *act it out*.

CC.2.MD.8

Erin used one $1 bill and 3 nickels to buy a marker.
How much money did Erin use to buy the marker?

Unlock the Problem

What do I need to find?	What information do I need to use?
how much money Erin used to buy the marker	Erin used one $1 bill and 3 nickels

Show how to solve the problem.

Draw to show the money that Erin used.

$1   5¢   5¢   5¢

Erin used ___$1.15___ to buy the marker.

**Use play coins and bills to solve.
Draw to show what you did.**

1. Zeke has one $1 bill, 2 dimes, and 1 nickel.   _____
   How much money does Zeke have?

CC.2.MD.8

Problem Solving • Money

Use play coins and bills to solve.
Draw to show what you did.

1. Sara has 2 quarters, 1 nickel, and two $1 bills.
   How much money does Sara have?   _____

2. Brad has one $1 bill, 4 dimes, and 2 nickels
   in his bank. How much money does Brad
   have in his bank?   _____

3. Mr. Morgan gives 1 quarter, 3 nickels, 4 pennies,
   and one $1 bill to the clerk. How much money
   does Mr. Morgan give the clerk?   _____

LESSON 92

Display Measurement Data

OBJECTIVE Measure the lengths of objects and use a line plot to display the measurement data.

CC.2.MD.9

Each X on the line plot is for the length of one book.

```
                        X
   X        X           X
   |_____|_____|_____|
   5        6           7           8
```

Lengths of Books in Inches

> One book is 5 inches long.
> One book is 6 inches long.
> Two books are 7 inches long.
> One book is 8 inches long.

---

1. Use an inch ruler. Measure and record the lengths of 4 pencils in inches.

1st pencil: _____ inches
2nd pencil: _____ inches
3rd pencil: _____ inches
4th pencil: _____ inches

2. Write the numbers and draw the Xs to complete the line plot.

```
   |_____|_____|_____|

   _____       _____       _____       _____
```

Lengths of Pencils in Inches

Display Measurement Data

1. Use an inch ruler.
   Measure and record the
   lengths of 4 different books
   in inches.

1st book: _____ inches	
2nd book: _____ inches	
3rd book: _____ inches	
4th book: _____ inches	

2. Make a line plot of the information above.
   Write a title for a line plot. Then
   write the numbers and draw the **X**s.

Problem Solving

3. Jesse measured the lengths of some strings.
   Use his list to complete the line plot.

Lengths of Strings
5 inches
7 inches
6 inches
8 inches
5 inches

Collect Data

OBJECTIVE Collect data in a survey and record that data in a tally chart.

CC.2.MD.10

You can take a survey to get information.

Which is your favorite sport?

Each tally mark stands for one person's answer. Count the tally marks.

Favorite Sport		
Sport	**Tally**	**Total**
soccer	llll	4
basketball	⊮⊮	5
football	lll	3

Elijah asked his classmates to choose their favorite breakfast food. He made this chart.

1. Write numbers to complete the chart.

Favorite Breakfast Food		
Food	**Tally**	**Total**
cereal	⊮⊮ lll	8
pancakes	llll	
toast	lll	
eggs	⊮⊮	

2. How many classmates chose pancakes?

_____ classmates

3. Which breakfast food did the fewest classmates choose?

_____

CC.2.MD.10

Collect Data

1. Take a survey. Ask 10 classmates how they got to school. Use tally marks to show their choices.

How We Got to School	
Way	**Tally**
walk	
bus	
car	
bike	

2. How many classmates rode in a bus to school?

_____ classmates

3. How many classmates rode in a car to school?

_____ classmates

4. In which way did the fewest classmates get to school?

_____

5. In which way did the most classmates get to school?

_____

6. Did more classmates get to school by walking or by riding in a car?

_____

How many more?

_____ more classmates

Lesson 93

LESSON 94

Read Picture Graphs

OBJECTIVE Interpret data in picture graphs and use that information to solve problems.

A picture graph uses pictures to show information.

Favorite Color

red					
blue					
green					

Key: Each ⬡ **stands for 1 child.**

The row with ___**blue**___ has 5 pictures.

So, ___5___ children chose blue.

Use the picture graph to answer the questions.

1. How many children chose red? _____ children

---

2. Did more children choose green
   or choose red? _____

---

3. Which color was chosen by
   the most children? _____

---

4. How many children in all chose
   a favorite color? _____ children

Read Picture Graphs

Use the picture graph to answer the questions.

Number of Books Read

Ryan	📖	📖	📖	📖		
Gwen	📖	📖				
Anna	📖	📖	📖	📖	📖	📖
Henry	📖	📖	📖			

Key: Each 📖 stands for 1 book.

1. How many books did Henry and Anna read? _____ books

2. How many more books did Ryan read than Gwen? _____ more books

3. How many fewer books did Gwen read than Anna? _____ fewer books

4. How many books did the four children read? _____ books

Problem Solving

Use the picture graph above. Write or draw to explain.

5. Carlos read 4 books. How many children read fewer books than Carlos?

_____ children

Make Picture Graphs

LESSON 95

OBJECTIVE Make picture graphs to represent data.

CC.2.MD.10

This picture graph uses 1 picture for each animal.
Draw a △ for each tally mark.

Animals at the Pet Store	
Animal	**Tally**
fish	IIII
hamster	II
turtle	III

Animals at the Pet Store				
fish	△	△	△	△
hamster	△	△		
turtle	△	△	△	

Key: Each △ stands for 1 animal.

How many turtles are at the pet store? __3__ turtles

1. Use the tally chart to complete the picture graph.
Draw a ☺ for each child.

Favorite Color	
Color	**Tally**
pink	⊪ℍ
yellow	III
blue	⊪ℍ

Favorite Color				
pink	☺	☺	☺	☺	☺
yellow				
blue				

Key: Each ☺ stands for 1 child.

2. Which color did the fewest children choose? _____

3. How many children chose pink? _____ children

4. How many more children chose blue
than chose yellow? _____ more children

CC.2.MD.10

Make Picture Graphs

I. Use the tally chart to complete the picture graph.

Draw a ☺ for each child.

Favorite Cookie	
Cookie	**Tally**
chocolate	III
oatmeal	I
peanut butter	IIII I
shortbread	IIII

Favorite Cookie					
chocolate					
oatmeal					
peanut butter					
shortbread					

Key: Each ☺ stands for 1 child.

2. How many children chose chocolate? _____ children

3. How many fewer children chose oatmeal than peanut butter? _____ fewer children

4. Which cookie did the most children choose?

_____

5. How many children chose a favorite cookie? _____ children

6. How many children chose oatmeal or shortbread? _____ children

Name _____

LESSON 96 **Read Bar Graphs**

OBJECTIVE Interpret data in bar graphs and use that information to solve problems.

CC.2.MD.10

Look at the number below the right end of each bar.

This number tells how many of each model Max has.

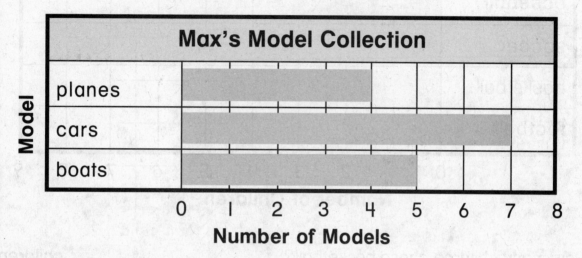

Max's Model Collection

Model: planes, cars, boats

Number of Models: 0 1 2 3 4 5 6 7 8

The bar for model cars ends at 7.

So, Max has __7__ car models.

Use the bar graph.

1. How many model planes does Max have?   _____ model planes

2. Does Max have more model boats
   or model planes?   more model _____

3. How many models does Max have?   _____ models

© Houghton Mifflin Harcourt Publishing Company

Measurement and Data

191

CC.2.MD.10

Read Bar Graphs

Use the bar graph.

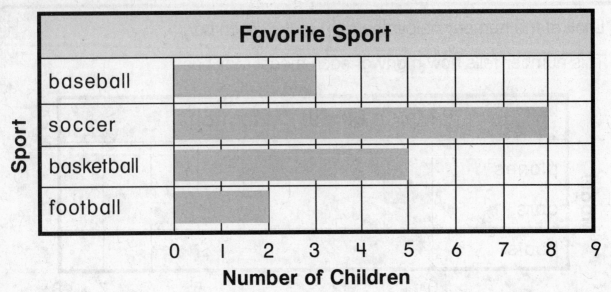

1. How many children chose basketball? _____ children

2. Which sport did the most children choose? _____

3. How many more children chose basketball
than baseball? _____ more children

4. Which sport did the fewest children choose? _____

5. How many children chose a sport that was not soccer? _____ children

Problem Solving

6. How many children chose
baseball or basketball? _____ children

LESSON 97

Make Bar Graphs

OBJECTIVE Make bar graphs to represent data.

CC.2.MD.10

These bar graphs show how many games Alex, Sarah, and Tony played.

- Alex played 5 games.

- Sarah played 3 games.

- Tony played 4 games.

Jim is making a bar graph to show the number of markers his friends have.

- Adam has 4 markers.

- Clint has 3 markers.

- Erin has 2 markers.

1. Write labels for the graph.

2. Draw bars in the graph to show the number of markers that Clint and Erin have.

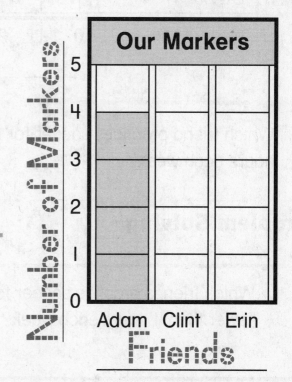

CC.2.MD.10

Make Bar Graphs

Maria asked her friends how many hours
they practice soccer each week.

- Jessie practices for 3 hours.
- Samantha practices for 5 hours.
- Victor practices for 2 hours.
- David practices for 6 hours.

I. Write a title and labels for the bar graph.

_____

2. Draw bars in the graph to show the data.

Jessie										
Victor										
Samantha										
David										

0 1 2 3 4 5 6 7 8 9 10

_____

3. Which friend practices soccer for the most
hours each week?

_____

Problem Solving

4. Which friends practice soccer for
fewer than 4 hours each week?

_____

LESSON 98 — Problem Solving · Display Data

OBJECTIVE Solve problems involving data by using the strategy *make a graph.*

CC.2.MD.10

The list shows how many hours
Morgan worked on her project.
Describe how the number of hours
changed from Week 1 to Week 4.

Week 1	1 hour
Week 2	2 hours
Week 3	3 hours
Week 4	4 hours

Unlock the Problem

What do I need to find?

how the number of ___hours___
changed from Week 1 to Week 4

What information do I need to use?

the number of ___hours___ Morgan
worked on her project each week

Show how to solve the problem.

Hours Worked on Project

Number of hours

5
4
3
2
1
0

Week 1   Week 2   Week 3   Week 4

Week

The number of hours _____

_____

Problem Solving • Display Data
Make a bar graph to solve the problem.

I. The list shows the number of books that Abby read each month. Describe how the number of books she read changed from February to May.

February	8 books
March	7 books
April	6 books
May	4 books

February										
March										
April										
May										

0   1   2   3   4   5   6   7   8   9   10

_____

The number of books _____

_____

2. How many books did Abby read in February and March? _____ books

3. How many fewer books did Abby read in April than in February? _____ fewer books

4. In which months did Abby read fewer than 7 books? _____

Name _____

LESSON 99

Three-Dimensional Shapes

OBJECTIVE Identify three-dimensional shapes.

CC.2.G.1

Three-dimensional objects come in different shapes.

sphere · **cone** · **cylinder** · **rectangular prism** · **cube**

Circle the objects that match the shape name.

1. rectangular prism

2. cylinder

3. cone

Three-Dimensional Shapes

Circle the objects that match
the shape name.

1. cube

2. cone

3. rectangular prism

4. cylinder

Problem Solving

5. Lisa draws a circle by tracing around the bottom
of a block. Which could be the shape of Lisa's block?
Circle the name of the shape.

      cone   cube   rectangular prism

LESSON 100

Attributes of Three-Dimensional Shapes

OBJECTIVE Identify and describe three-dimensional shapes according to the number of faces, edges, and vertices.

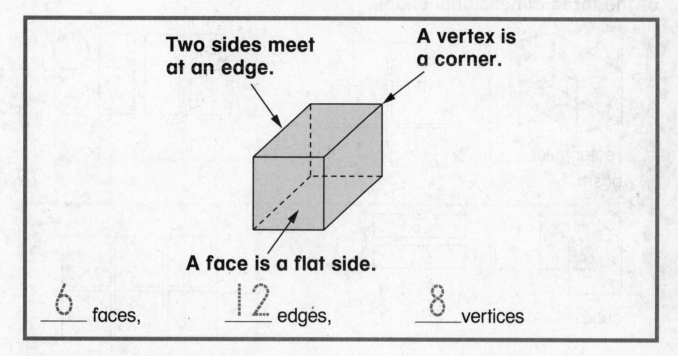

Two sides meet at an edge.

A vertex is a corner.

A face is a flat side.

__6__ faces,   __12__ edges,   __8__ vertices

Write how many for each.

	faces	edges	vertices
1. cube	_____	_____	_____
2. rectangular prism	_____	_____	_____

CC.2.G.1

Attributes of Three-Dimensional Shapes

Circle the set of shapes that are the faces
of the three-dimensional shape.

Problem Solving

4. Kevin keeps his marbles in a container that
has the shape of a cube. He wants to paint
each face a different color. How many
different paint colors does he need? _____ different paint colors

LESSON 101

Two-Dimensional Shapes

OBJECTIVE Name 3-, 4-, 5-, and 6-sided shapes according to the number of sides and vertices.

 CC.2.G.1

Count sides and vertices.
A pentagon has 5 sides.

pentagon

A hexagon has 6 vertices.

hexagon

Write the number of sides and the number of vertices.

1. triangle

_____ sides

_____ vertices

2. rectangle

_____ sides

_____ vertices

3. quadrilateral

_____ sides

_____ vertices

4. pentagon

_____ sides

_____ vertices

CC.2.G.1

Two-Dimensional Shapes

Write the number of sides and the
number of vertices. Then write
the name of the shape.

pentagon	triangle
hexagon	quadrilateral

1.

_____ sides

_____ vertices

_____

2.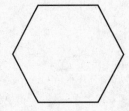

_____ sides

_____ vertices

_____

3.

_____ sides

_____ vertices

_____

4.

_____ sides

_____ vertices

_____

5.

_____ sides

_____ vertices

_____

6.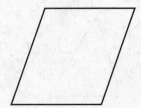

_____ sides

_____ vertices

_____

Problem Solving

Solve. Draw or write to explain.

7. Oscar is drawing a picture of a house.
He draws a pentagon shape for a window.
How many sides does his window have? _____ sides

Angles in Two-Dimensional Shapes

OBJECTIVE Identify angles in two-dimensional shapes.

CC.2.G.1

Two sides meet and form an angle.

There are ____4____ angles in a square.

angle ➡

Circle the angles in each shape.
Write how many.

1.

_____ angles

2.

_____ angles

3.

_____ angles

CC.2.G.1

Angles in Two-Dimensional Shapes

Circle the angles in each shape.
Write how many.

1.

_____ **angles**

2.

_____ **angles**

3.

_____ **angles**

4.

_____ **angles**

Problem Solving

5. Logan drew 2 two-dimensional shapes that had 8 angles in all. Draw shapes Logan could have drawn.

Sort Two-Dimensional Shapes

OBJECTIVE Sort two-dimensional shapes according to their attributes.

CC.2.G.1

Circle the shapes with 5 sides.

4 sides   3 sides   5 sides   6 sides

Circle the shapes with fewer than 5 angles.

3 angles   6 angles   4 angles   5 angles

Circle the shapes that match the rule.

1. Shapes with 4 sides

2. Shapes with more than 4 angles

Sort Two-Dimensional Shapes

Circle the shapes that match the rule.

1. Shapes with fewer than 5 sides

2. Shapes with more than 4 sides

3. Shapes with 4 angles

4. Shapes with fewer than 6 angles

Problem Solving

Circle the correct shape.

5. Tammy drew a shape with more than 3 angles.
It is not a hexagon. Which shape did Tammy draw?

Partition Rectangles

LESSON 104

OBJECTIVE Partition rectangles into equal-size squares and find the total number of these squares.

CC.2.G.2

How many color tiles cover this rectangle?

Make a row of color tiles on the rectangle.
Trace around the square tiles.

How many squares? ___3___ squares

Use color tiles to cover the rectangle.
Trace around the square tiles. Write how many.

1.

Number of rows: _____

Number of columns: _____

Total: _____ squares

2.

Number of rows: _____

Number of columns: _____

Total: _____ squares

CC.2.G.2

Partition Rectangles

Use color tiles to cover the rectangle.
Trace around the square tiles.
Write how many.

1.

Number of rows: _____

Number of columns: _____

Total: _____ square tiles

2.

Number of rows: _____

Number of columns: _____

Total: _____ square tiles

Problem Solving

Solve. Write or draw to explain.

3. Nina wants to put color tiles on a square. 3 color tiles fit across the top of the square. How many rows and columns of squares will Nina need? How many color tiles will she use in all?

Number of rows: _____

Number of columns: _____

Total: _____ square tiles

_____ tiles

LESSON 105 | # Equal Parts

OBJECTIVE Identify and name equal parts of circles and rectangles as halves, thirds, or fourths.

CC.2.G.3

You can divide a whole into equal parts.

<u>2</u> equal parts

halves

<u>3</u> equal parts

thirds

<u>4</u> equal parts

fourths

Write how many equal parts there are in the whole.
Write halves, thirds, or fourths to name the equal parts.

1.

<u>4</u> equal parts

fourths

2.

_____ equal parts

_____

3.

_____ equal parts

_____

4.

_____ equal parts

_____

5.

_____ equal parts

_____

6.

_____ equal parts

_____

Equal Parts

Write how many equal parts there are in the whole.
Write halves, thirds, or fourths to name the equal parts.

1.

_____ equal parts

_____

2.

_____ equal parts

_____

3.

_____ equal parts

_____

4.

_____ equal parts

_____

5.

_____ equal parts

_____

6.

_____ equal parts

_____

Problem Solving

7. Sort the shapes.

• Draw an X on the shapes
that do not show equal parts.

• Circle the shapes that
show halves.

Name _____

Trace to show the equal parts.

2 equal parts
2 halves

3 equal parts
3 thirds

4 equal parts
4 fourths

Draw to show equal parts.

1. halves

2. thirds

3. halves

4. fourths

CC.2.G.3

Show Equal Parts of a Whole

Draw to show equal parts.

1. halves

2. fourths

3. thirds

4. thirds

5. halves

6. fourths

7. fourths

8. halves

9. thirds

Problem Solving

Solve. Write or draw to explain.

10. Joe has one sandwich. He cuts the sandwich into fourths. How many pieces of sandwich does he have?

_____ pieces

Describe Equal Parts

OBJECTIVE Identify and describe one equal part as a half of, a third of, or a fourth of a whole.

CC.2.G.3

One equal part of each shape is shaded.

A half of the shape is shaded.

A third of the shape is shaded.

A fourth of the shape is shaded.

Draw to show halves.
Color a half of the shape.

1.

2.

Draw to show fourths.
Color a fourth of the shape.

3.

4.

Describe Equal Parts

Draw to show halves.
Color a half of the shape.

1.

2.

Draw to show thirds.
Color a third of the shape.

3.

4.

Draw to show fourths.
Color a fourth of the shape.

5.

6.

Problem Solving

7. Circle all the shapes that have a
    third of the shape shaded.

Name _____

 Problem Solving · Equal Shares

OBJECTIVE Solve problems involving wholes divided into equal shares by using the strategy *draw a diagram.*

 CC.2.G.3

Two gardens are the same size. Each garden is divided into halves, but the gardens are divided differently. How might the gardens be divided?

Unlock the Problem	
What do I need to find? how the gardens are divided	**What information do I need to use?** There are ___2___ gardens. Each garden is divided into halves .

Show how to solve the problem.

Draw to show your answer.

I. Sophie has two pieces of paper that are the same size. She wants to divide each piece into fourths. What are two different ways she can divide the pieces of paper?

CC.2.G.3

Problem Solving • Equal Shares

Draw to show your answer.

I. Max has square pizzas that are the same size.
What are two different ways he can divide the
pizzas into fourths?

---

2. Lia has two pieces of paper that are the same size.
What are two different ways she can divide the
pieces of paper into halves?

---

3. Frank has two crackers that are the same size.
What are two different ways he can divide the
cracker into thirds?